WORLD OF 1001 MYSTERIES

about the author

RUSSELL STANNARD is Professor of Physics at the Open University Milton Keynes. He has travelled widely in Europe and the United States of America, researching high energy nuclear physics. In 1968 he received the Templeton UK project award and has recently spent a year in America as Visiting Fellow at the Center of Theological Inquiry, Princeton.

Married with four children of his own and three step-children, he believes that the elements of physics can and should be introduced to children in an exciting and accessible way. *The Time and Space of Uncle Albert*, his first book for young readers, was shortlisted for both The Science Book Award and the Whitbread Award (Children's category). *Black Holes and Uncle Albert* is his second book which explores Einstein's theories and can be read as a companion volume or on its own. *Here I Am!* is his response to the challenging question: can science and religious belief co-exist in the modern world? *World of 1001 Mysteries* introduces Phusis, a modern-day Scherezade, who tells the stories of the genuine mysteries of physics, in order to try to save the universe itself from destruction.

WORLD OF
1001 MYSTERIES

Russell Stannard

Illustrated by Chris Priestley

faber and faber
LONDON · BOSTON

First published in 1993
by Faber and Faber Limited
3 Queen Square London WC1N 3AU
This paperback edition first published in 1994

Printed in England by Clays Ltd, St Ives plc

Russell Stannard is hereby identified as author of this work in accordance with
Section 77 of the Copyright, Designs and Patents Act 1988

A CIP record for this book is available from the British Library

ISBN 0 571 17049 8

2 4 6 8 10 9 7 5 3 1

My thanks

to those who, long ago, created the stories of *1001 Arabian Nights*, and were the inspiration for this book;

to the children of Linslade Middle School and The Cedars School, Linslade, who helped me in the writing of it;

to my wife, Maggi, for her continuing support.

Contents

Prologue   *Goodbye World!*   1

1   *The Crafty Master of Disguise*   12

2   *What's the Matter?*   33

3   *Nothing Is What It Seems*   50

4   *Time Marches On – Or Does It?*   71

5   *Now You See It; Now You Don't*   95

6   *How's That for a Bargain!*   121

Epilogue   *Only a Beginning . . .*   148

Prologue

Goodbye World!

The world was to be destroyed! Not just the Earth. The whole universe had to go – the Sun, the Moon, the stars, space, time, life.

It all came as a great shock. First there was the news that our universe was not alone; there were lots of universes. The others lay beyond our space and time; that's why we hadn't known about them. They were all different; they each had their own spaces, and times, and laws of nature. They belonged to an organization called the Federation of Universes. We were members too, though until now no one had thought to tell us.

Rule 184930/56/f in the Federation's Rule Book states: *Universes must be kept up-to-date*. That was the problem. Our universe had been around for 15,000 million Earth years; it had now passed its sell-by date. There was nothing for it, declared the Federation; it had to be renewed. That's what they called it: 'renewed'. In plain talk it meant the universe had to be destroyed to make way for a brand new model. After all, it was argued, much better universes were now on offer: simpler to run; fully computerized; complete with all the latest features. Planets, for example, can now be designed to any shape. (Round

ones are thought these days to be very boring.)
Chemical elements? Pick and mix – no end of choice.
And you should see the range of modern rainbows –
any colours you like.

The other difficulty was with rule 284619/61/b:
Universes must at all times be properly looked after. The
universe was in a mess. It was dirty and polluted –
not fit to live in. Oil supplies were being used up;
trees were being burnt. No one seemed to care; no
one took a pride in the place any more.

Mind you, the Federation tried to be fair. It didn't
carry out its decisions right away. There was an
appeals process. Any universe due to be destr – er . . .
renewed – would receive a visit from the Appeals
Judge. If there were any forms of intelligent life in the
universe, he had to contact them to find out if there
might be any special reason why the decision should
not be confirmed. On his return to the Federation's
headquarters at Elsewhere, he would then announce
his decision.

If the order was to go ahead, it was then up to Fred.
Fred was the Head Exterminator. 'Getting rid of
universes? Nothing to it, mate,' says Fred. 'Not now
I've got my Schlurpit* Heavy Duty World Disposal
Unit, Mark II. Much better than the old Mark I.
Burped something terrible that last one. Don't get me
wrong. It'd swallow the universe, like. But then just
when you thought it had finished . . . It'd let you

---

* 'Schlurpit' is an Elsewherean word, pronounced with an *intake*
of breath – just as you might say it if you were trying to have a
drink at the same time.

have one. Cor, talk about pong! Stuck to your clothes, it did. But not this one. No, not this beauty. She takes in a whole universe, squashes it down to a dot, then one quick schluu . . . uurp – KERPOW! Nothing. It's as if that universe had never existed. Here, do you know what the secret is? I'll tell you: black hole technology. That's it. That's the name of the game, these days. Can't beat it. I'd never use anything else now. Well, what I say is, if you're going to do a job, you might as well do it properly. And another thing . . .'

From which you will gather that it was never a good idea to ask Fred too much about his job. He could go on for ever about the universes he has removed from the Federation's register. His Mark II Unit alone has notched up 1,000.

At the point where our story begins, the Appeals Judge has almost come to the end of his tour of the universe. He has spoken with every form of intelligent life – from the ten-headed parallel processors of Pollux, to the Gemini geniuses who plug tiny computers straight into their brains.

The Judge is tired and fed up. Everywhere he has had to listen to the same snivelling complaints: people concerned with one thing only – how to save their skins. 'Why can't they face up to the simple fact that, by today's standards, their universe is a dud?' he would ask himself.

Earth was to be his last stop. The visit got off to a bad start. All the big countries wanted the honour of being the host. A major row broke out. The Judge was shocked. 'Are you sure this "human being" life-form has not been wrongly classed as "intelligent"?' he asked Headquarters on his videophone. In the end he called for a map of the world – and stuck a pin in it. And that was how he came to set up his office in the saloon bar of the Red Lion Inn, overlooking the green at Bumbledon-with-Ketchup. It was to this little-known village, tucked away in the Cotswold Hills of central England, that the Secretary General of the United Nations and the heads of state had to journey to give their evidence and make their arguments.

They first complained about the shape of the table they had to sit round; they then objected to the other people they had to sit next to; then they demanded to have 'talks about talks'. When all this was brushed aside by the Judge, who was getting crosser by the minute, they at last got down to 'protesting in the strongest terms', 'expressing outrage', and declaring that the decision of the Federation was 'unacceptable'. None of which had the slightest effect on the Judge.

'Right,' he announced. 'If that's all you have to say for yourselves, the hearing is at an end.' With that he snapped his file shut. 'Now get out – the lot of you!'

Everyone was in despair. Protests ranged from a polite HANDS OFF BASILDON tea party at the local church hall, to gangs of tough-looking youths roaming the streets of Liverpool chanting, 'We are the champions. Watch it, Feds; we know where you live.' Which, of course, was not true; no one had any idea where Elsewhere was, except that it was 'beyond' *all* universes.

It was evening. The heads of state and their guards had left in their black limos. The newspaper and TV reporters packed away their things. As the last of them left, Bumbledon breathed a sigh of relief. Only the litter strewn across the green bore witness to the events of recent days.

A lone figure sat on the bench beside the pond. Her name was Phusis.* She watched as the Sun set behind the school where she taught. Phusis enjoyed her job. She loved the children; they were such fun, so eager to learn. But the work was tiring, and she was thankful at the end of the day to come out here for a quiet sit down before making her way home. She was glad all the visitors had gone.

But had they? A tall figure, dressed in black, holding a walking stick, was coming along the path. She did not recognize him. As he reached her, he stopped. 'Excuse me,' he said. 'I wonder whether you would mind if I . . .' He nodded towards the bench.

'Of course not,' she replied, making room.

He seemed grateful for the chance to sit down. 'Ah, that's better,' he sighed. He was quite old.

'Lovely sunset tonight,' Phusis said.

'Yes, it is,' he replied.

'New around here?' she asked.

'Yes. Just passing through.'

---

* Yes, another funny name, but not Elsewherean this time. It's pronounced 'Foosis'.

'It's a pity you have to see it like this,' she said, as a flurry of chocolate-bar and cigarette wrappings were whipped up around their feet by the gentle breeze. 'What a mess. The green used to be so neat and tidy. I sometimes think the Federation has a point,' she sighed.

The stranger raised an eyebrow. 'How do you mean?' he asked.

'Oh, nothing. It's just . . . Well, they say we've got our world into a mess; we don't look after it. With all this rubbish here, I reckon they're right.'

He smiled. 'I've been saying that for some time. Nice to hear someone agree with me for a change.'

'Why? Are things bad where you come from? Where *are* you from – if you don't mind my asking?'

'Elsewhere. A place called Elsewhere.'

'Else . . .!' Phusis sprang to her feet in alarm. 'You . . . You . . .'

'What's the matter?' he asked. 'Did I say something? Please . . .'

'You're the JUDGE!' she exclaimed.

His eyes twinkled. 'I thought you knew. Sorry. I should have introduced myself. Yes, I'm the Appeals Judge. Please. Won't you sit down?'

'But . . .'

She resumed her seat.

'But what?' he said. 'I'm not what you expected?'

'I don't know what I expected,' she said. 'I suppose I didn't expect you to look so . . .'

'. . . ordinary?' he suggested. 'You didn't expect an Elsewherean to look human?'

'Well, no.'

'Don't be fooled, my dear. This is not what I normally look like. This is not the real me; it's just a tactile holographic reconstruction .'

'A what?'

'A hologram. You know. Those three-dimensional images. I have this device that senses out the form of life I am talking to, and it surrounds the real me with a hologram looking like that form of life.'

'How clever!' exclaimed Phusis. 'I'd love to know how it works.'

'That would be a bit difficult to explain – given the state of your scientific knowledge. Not yours personally, I mean. No offence. No, I mean the state of scientific knowledge in this universe.'

'But if you're just a hologram,' continued Phusis, 'You're ... well, you're just an illusion. There's nothing actually there.' With that she reached out to wave her hand through his head – and promptly slapped the Judge round the face!

'OH!' she cried. 'Oh, I'm terribly sorry. I didn't think . . .'

'No, you did not,' he growled. He was *very* put out. 'I said – did I not? – that it was a *tactile* hologram. Tactile – you can *touch* it, *feel* it.'

'But I've never heard of such . . .'

'All right, all right,' he grumbled, settling himself down again. 'No, I suppose tactile holograms are not something you can have in a universe of this sort.'

There was an awkward silence. Eventually Phusis cleared her throat: 'Ahem. Why do you use a hologram? Why not look your normal self?'

He gave her a hard, somewhat menacing look.

'That would not be wise. Take it from me. It's better this way. It . . . it helps people to feel more comfortable, more at ease.' Then he added with a snarl, 'It also puts them off their guard – helps me to see them as they *really* are.'

Phusis wondered what he meant by that, but decided to change the subject. 'How . . . how long do you intend staying? I notice everyone seems to have left this evening.'

'Yes, the hearings are over. I leave tomorrow.'

'Oh. Do I take it you've . . . made up your mind?'

He nodded gravely.

'I see,' she said. 'Can I ask what you've decided?'

A hint of a sneer flickered across his face.

'Oh,' said Phusis quietly.

She shuddered slightly – she did not know whether through fear, anger or the cold. The Sun had now set, and the autumn breeze playing with the scraps of paper at their feet had turned chilly.

She wanted to protest – to cry out that the world was a wonderful, wonderful place. That's what she always told her children. This universe was different from most of the others; it was the home of living creatures – the home of *people*. You can't just go around killing people.

But she daren't; she had read in the papers about the Judge's terrible rages. Besides, hadn't all the clever prime ministers and presidents tried protesting? And that hadn't got them anywhere. No, she mustn't protest.

It was then that a plan began to form in Phusis's mind . . .

8

'Ah well,' she said in a resigned tone. 'To be honest, I can't say I'm surprised.'

'No?'

'Oh, no. You can't stop progress. And there's no denying our old universe is pretty long in the tooth. 15,000 million years: that's so long my children can't *begin* to imagine how long it is.'

'Your children? How many do you have?' he asked.

'Twenty-five.'

'What! You have twenty-five children?'

She laughed. 'Not *my* children. Well, not exactly. No, I teach over there,' she said, pointing out the school-house across the green.

'What do you teach?' he asked.

'I have to teach everything. But mostly I enjoy teaching science.'

They sat in silence for a while.

'Tell me,' she said eventually. 'When is the . . . you know. When will it happen?'

'As soon as I get back – tomorrow lunchtime.'

'Yes, well, I suppose there's no point in delaying things once the decision's been made.'

He smiled. 'I must say, it's refreshing to find somebody who thinks so soundly and sensibly. Very positive. I only wish there were more like you; it would make my job a lot easier, I can tell you.'

'Mind you,' murmured Phusis to herself. 'That's a pity . . . tomorrow lunchtime, you say?'

'Why? What's the problem?'

'Oh, nothing. It's just . . . well, it's just that in my science lessons I've got to the point where I'm about to tell the children about light – crafty light . . .'

'Sorry. Light, did you say?' he asked.

'Yes.'

'But, you said something about *crafty*. Light being *crafty*. I'm sorry, you've lost me . . .'

'The properties of light: how it's always in a hurry, how it cheats when it races, how it is the great master of disguise . . .'

'I . . . I don't follow. How can light *cheat*? And what's all this about disguises?'

By now Phusis had stood up. 'I must be going. It's got quite cold. It's been nice meeting you . . .'

'But wait,' protested the Judge. 'I insist on hearing what you were about to say.'

'I'm sorry, I can't do that now. I'm cold; I'm shivering. Look – goose-pimples. Besides, I have things to do . . . But I tell you what: I could come back tomorrow, if you like – after school. I could tell you the same as I've told the children . . .' Her voice trailed off. 'Oh, no. Of course I can't. I was forgetting. There isn't going to be a tomorrow – not a tomorrow evening.' She shrugged her shoulders. 'Ah well.' She gave a little laugh. 'I guess you'll never know.'

Phusis had a far-away look in her eye. '*Crafty*, did I say?' she continued. 'Light is a GENIUS!' And with that she turned on her heel, and walked swiftly away.

'No, no,' muttered the Judge after her, waving his walking stick at her. 'Wait! Wait a minute, damn it!' He rummaged in his coat pockets. Then: 'COME BACK HERE!' he thundered. His voice echoed round the green. The windows of the Red Lion rattled. The branches of the trees quivered, releasing a shower of brown leaves. Phusis felt her blood run cold. She froze in her tracks. By the time she had meekly returned to where he was sitting, he was calmly looking at his pocket diary.

'As I thought,' he remarked. 'I don't have anything special on tomorrow. I can, therefore, delay my return for twenty-four hours. And why shouldn't I? All this travel. I deserve a day off. I eat at 7.30 p.m. So you will be good enough to report at 9.00 p.m. sharp.' He nodded briefly in the direction of the Red Lion. He raised his hat to her slightly. 'Good night,' he said, and waved her away.

The Judge lit up a pipe, stroked his chin, and became lost in thought.

Phusis hurried home.

'Oh dear. What have I got myself into?' she wondered.

1 *The Crafty Master of Disguise*

Phusis arrived early. She was shown into the saloon bar.

'Where is everyone?' she asked the landlord. 'It's usually so crowded this time of an evening.'

'Not since *he* came,' was the reply. 'This room is for his own personal use. That's what he said. All the regulars have to use the Public Bar.' He shrugged. 'There's no arguing with his sort. Anyway,' he added glumly. 'What's the point? It'll all be over by tomorrow. That's when he's booked out for. Then it's the chop, right?' He made a movement with his hand, as if to cut his throat. 'You might as well sit down. He's not long started his dinner.'

'Oh, but I thought he said . . .'

In fact, it was nearly 10 o'clock before the Judge came wandering in. He looked at Phusis with some surprise. 'Oh, yes, I was forgetting. I beg your pardon . . .' He searched for her name.

'Phusis. My name is Phusis,' she said timidly.

'Ah, yes. Now what was it . . .? Light? Something you wanted to tell me about light? By the way, it won't take long, will it? I do have to make an early start tomorrow.' He settled into an armchair and lit his pipe.

'Well,' said Phusis. 'Light is special. It holds the World Speed Record. It travels through empty space at 186,000 miles per second.'

'Per second?' murmured the Judge. 'Earth seconds, of course. That means . . . Hmmm . . . I see what you mean. That is quite fast. Quite a target for the others to aim at, eh?'

'Ah,' said Phusis. 'But that's the interesting thing about this record: there's no point in aiming at it; it can never be broken.'

'Don't be silly. Of course it can be broken. It *will* be broken. Or at least, it *would* have got broken, one day, if the universe were not due to be . . . you know . . . That's how it is with records. They *always* get broken.'

'But not this one,' insisted Phusis. 'It's not like . . .'

'Look, my dear,' the Judge interrupted. 'If you want something to go faster, you push it. You want it to go faster still? You push harder and longer. There's no limit to how hard and how long you can push, so it stands to reason there's no limit to how fast you can make something go.'

'But there *is* a limit,' said Phusis. 'May I . . .?' With that she lifted a plastic case on to the table and opened it.

'What's that you've got?' asked the Judge.

'A videodisc player. I thought it might come in handy. I use it all the time at school. I wanted you to see something I was showing the kids this afternoon.'

She plugged it in and switched on. A picture came up on to the screen. It showed an enormous straight

13

pipe stretching off into the distance.

'This is a machine two miles long. It's designed to make particles go fast. It is fed with the tiniest particles in our universe; they're called *electrons*. They weigh hardly anything, so it's easy to accelerate them. It's much easier to get something going if you push on something light rather than something heavy . . .'

'Of course, of course,' interrupted the Judge impatiently. 'I'm not one of your children. Get to the point.'

'Sorry . . . Well, all I'm saying is that if any kind of particle is going to beat the speed record set by light, it has to be the electron – and it will be done in a machine like this.'

'So?'

'It *can't* be done. No matter how hard or how long the machine pushes on the electron, it never quite catches up with the light beam. It can get to a tiny, tiny fraction of a percent of the speed of light, but it can never quite reach it – let alone exceed it.'

'But why?' asked the Judge, clearly not convinced. 'It doesn't make sense.'

'Ah, but it does make sense,' said Phusis. 'Light is crafty. It has arranged for this to be a handicap race.'

'What's that? A *handicap* race?'

'Well,' explained Phusis, 'in horse racing, if a horse keeps winning its races, they make it carry an extra weight. That slows it down in its next race so as to give the other horses a chance. (Well, it gets boring if the same horse *always* wins.) The extra weight is called a *handicap*. The stronger and faster the horse,

14

the greater the handicap it has to carry.'

'But what has this to do with electrons?'

'I'm getting there, sir,' said Phusis. 'The point is that electrons, and any other particle that tries to race against light – they find themselves in a handicap race. As soon as they pick up speed, they get an extra weight to carry. Faster still? An even heavier weight. And, of course, the heavier the weight the harder it is to make the particle go a bit faster. Those electrons in that machine,' said Phusis, pointing to the screen, 'by the time they reach the end of their two-mile race track, they weigh 40,000 times as much as they did at the beginning! And the beauty of it all is that it's an *instant* handicap race. It's not that you get your extra handicap in the next race, based on your past performance. No, you get it in this race. The faster you go in *this* race, the more weight you carry; it happens automatically.'

'But what about light?' asked the Judge. 'What sort of handicap does *it* have to carry?'

'None,' replied Phusis. 'None at all. That's why it always wins. That's why its speed record will never fall.'

'But that's not fair,' declared the Judge.

'Exactly. That's what I was saying. Light is very crafty. It cheats.' So saying, she switched off the videodisc player, and began to pack it away.

'Hmmm,' observed the Judge. 'That was interesting.'

'Yes,' she said. 'My children find it fascinating. Mind you, not so fascinating as the way light is always working out how to take short cuts. Now that they find *really* interesting.'

'Oh, what's that?'

'Oh, nothing,' she said, putting on her coat.

'No, tell me. I'm interested. Short cuts, you say? What do you mean?'

'It would take too long to explain. Your early start tomorrow, remember. Besides I would need a different videodisc to show you. Pity. Anyway, it's been very nice talking with you. Good night. Have a safe journey . . .'

'No, no wait,' he said hastily. 'Um . . . Let me see . . .'

'But you have to go back tomorrow,' said Phusis.

'I don't *have* to,' he declared crossly. 'I don't *have* to do *anything*.'

'Well, if you did decide to stay on another day . . .'

'I might . . . Yes, I might just do that. *One* more day. Only the one, of course. And then I really ought to get back . . . Short cuts, you say? Light taking short cuts, eh? Sounds intriguing.' He seemed gently amused. 'Right then. Tomorrow night. Here at the same time.'

'What time would that be? I was here at 9.00 p.m. – as arranged.'

His eyes flashed angrily. She bit her lip.

'You will get here at the same time, please,' he said coldly.

Phusis hurried home. 'Well, at least that saves the world for another day.'

The next evening, the *second* after their meeting on the green, Phusis arrived promptly at the saloon bar of the Red Lion. Again she brought her videodisc player. She was trying it out when the Judge strolled into the room – at 9.30 p.m.

'So, we meet again,' he said as he settled into his chair. 'And what have you to say for yourself this evening?'

'Well, I was telling you yesterday about how fast light is. Light is our messenger. It travels to us from distant objects and tells us what objects are out there.'

'I had noticed that,' observed the Judge. 'A very useful feature that. Unusual for an old-fashioned universe like yours. These older models aren't normally fitted out with light. Normally you have to *feel* your way round them. Painfully slow business. Can be *literally* painful,' he laughed ruefully. 'I've banged a few shins in my time, I can tell you.'

'Anyway, as I was saying,' continued Phusis, 'light comes to us with its messages very fast – not just because it travels fast, but because it knows the quickest routes. Let me show you.'

On the screen appeared a picture showing a boy looking up at a bird in a tree.

'The light comes from the bird to the boy in a straight line,' said Phusis. 'That's the shortest distance and so it's the quickest route.'

'I know, I know,' said the Judge. 'What of it?'

'Ah, but take what's happening here,' continued Phusis hastily.

Now the boy was looking at a fish resting on the bottom of a pool.

'What route does the light take to get to the boy

17

now – from the fish?' she asked.

'A straight line, of course. The quickest route. Look, is this all you came . . .'

'No. I'm sorry. That's not quite right. It isn't a straight line.'

'It's not? But you said it took the quickest . . .'

'Yes it does. But light travels more slowly through water.'

'Oh.'

'Yes, it's like being able to run faster on dry land than you can swim. So to get to its destination in the shortest time – to get to the boy's eye – it's better to take a different route – a longer total distance, but one that is shorter in the water.' With that, Phusis got the videodisc to display the actual path taken by the light – a path that was bent.

The Judge looked puzzled. 'Here. Let me have a go with this thing. How does it work?'

Phusis showed him how to operate the player and how it could be used to try out different possible

paths between the fish and the boy's eye. In the top right-hand corner of the screen it recorded the total time light would have taken to travel such a path. The Judge experimented with different paths. Sure enough, the path actually chosen by the ray of light was the quickest.

'How interesting,' he murmured. 'Yes, that's clever. It's as if the light knows *in advance* where it's going to land up – at the boy's eye. It then sets off in just the right direction – having already worked out the quickest route to get there. How odd.'

He sat back in his chair and slowly stroked his chin. 'Thank you, my dear. That was quite . . . diverting.' He got up. 'Now if you don't mind . . .'

'Of course,' said Phusis. 'If you like, I could come back tomorrow . . .'

'No, no. I'm off tomorrow, remember,' said the Judge.

'But I haven't told you about . . .'

The Judge silenced her with a glance. She quietly packed up the videodisc player and left.

'So much for the plan,' she thought to herself as she trudged home. 'Stupid! I might have known I couldn't fool the likes of him for long. So that's it: no more playing for time.'

The following morning, Phusis made her way to the school with a heavy heart. There hardly seemed any point to taking lessons – it being the final day. She spent the first period trying to comfort the older children. They, of course, had read all about the end of the world in the newspapers, so it came as no surprise to them to learn that it was set for today – as soon as the Judge got back to Elsewhere. The little ones carried on drawing and painting as if nothing were the matter; the grown-ups had all agreed there was no point in upsetting them.

In the middle of the lesson, the telephone rang in the school office. It was the Judge. He wanted further details about the videodisc player: could it deal with different cases to the one that Phusis had shown him the previous evening – light not only going through water but through glass, and diamond, and quartz – and light going through different shaped objects rather than flat ones like the surface of the pool? Phusis told him that all this was possible.

'Right. Bring it round after school, will you,' he said.

'But I thought . . .'

'Do as I ask.'

'Yes, sir,' said Phusis in some surprise.

So it was on the *third* evening Phusis again found herself in the saloon bar of the Red Lion. The Judge turned up – on time. It soon became clear that he had been deeply puzzled by what she had earlier said about light always taking short cuts. He had some ideas he wanted to try out. With Phusis's aid, he learned how to use the videodisc to find out how light would travel through glass wedges, quartz prisms, diamond crystals, or troughs of water.

Each time, without a hint of a mistake, light got to its goal by the quickest route.

On the *fourth* night the Judge tried to outwit the light beam by making it go through one object after another – each one made of a different material, with a different speed of light. But again, no matter how he changed the distances and the angles, the light beam never made a mistake.

On the *fifth* night he tried lenses – curved surfaces instead of flat ones. 'Surely that will fool the light beam,' he thought. But no.

On the *sixth*, he thought he would be extra cunning. He made the light go through a material where, as the light went more and more deeply into it, its speed *gradually* changed, bit by bit. Phusis angered the Judge by laughing. 'You'll never trick light that way,' she cried. 'Light often has to do that. On a hot day, the air closer to the ground is hotter than it is higher up, and light passes more quickly through it down there. This means rays of light close to the ground get bent. That's how we get mirages.'

'All right, all right,' muttered the Judge, clearly annoyed with the whole thing. 'Waste of time. It's obvious really. Properties gradually changing; light follows a curved path. It's no big deal.'

'No, of course not,' said Phusis. 'I'm sure you've come across that sort of thing many times.'

'Of course. Well, no . . . not exactly. Not in the other universes I've had to see to. But it's nothing special.'

'No. I agree. It was good of you to show an interest,' she said.

'Well, even someone like myself needs a little time for relaxation – playing a few games – that sort of thing.'

'Naturally. All work and no play . . .'

'All what?' he asked.

'Nothing. Just one of those silly sayings we have here on Earth.'

'Oh.'

'So, tomorrow you're off. The Big Day and all that. Sorry I upset your plans a bit.'

'No matter,' said the Judge rising. 'It's been a real pleasure talking to you, Phusis.'

'And I too have enjoyed our chats. Pity we couldn't have carried on a bit longer. One more day would have made all the difference.'

'Oh? Why's that?' he asked suspiciously.

She shrugged. 'Oh, it doesn't matter. As you said, it's no big deal to have light following a curved path through a material, like the air, where the properties are gradually changing. I shouldn't have wasted your time with such trivia. But to have a curved light path in *empty* space, now there is a wonder to behold.'

'Come again? How can light follow a curved path in empty space? We have already checked out that it always takes the quickest path in empty space – and that must be a straight line.'

Phusis smiled. 'Oh no,' she said. 'The space of this universe is much more subtle than that.'

'How do you mean?'

'Well,' said Phusis, 'it's like this . . . Oh no. I can't show you . . . not tonight. Wrong disc. I didn't realize we might get on to this . . . I don't suppose there's any chance . . .? No, of course not . . .'

On the *seventh* evening, the videodisc player showed the Earth as a tiny dot in the sky surrounded by stars.

'I want you to imagine that light from this star over here has to travel to the Earth,' said Phusis. 'On the way it has to pass close by this other star. Which path will it take?'

'Is the space empty – apart from the stars?' asked the Judge. 'No air or anything between the stars and the Earth?'

'You can assume that.'

'Well, in that case, what's the problem?'

He sat down at the player and got it to draw a straight line from the distant star, passing close by the one in between, and so on to the Earth.

There flashed up on to the screen the word:

WRONG

This was followed by:

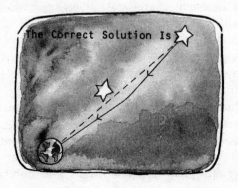

The screen displayed a path that started out from the star at a slightly different angle to the line the Judge had drawn. It went straight for a while, but when it got close to the star in the middle, it curved towards it. After that, it became straight again before ending up at the Earth.

'That's stupid!' declared the Judge angrily. 'That path has got a kink in it.'

'That's right,' said Phusis. 'It's because of gravity. The star in the middle has gravity and that affects the space around it.'

'But the space is *empty*,' protested the Judge. 'That's what you said.'

'Yes, I know,' said Phusis. 'But even empty space is affected by gravity. Space affected by gravity slows down light. So, just as it's not a good idea for light to spend long passing through water where its speed is lower, it doesn't want to spend long going through "slowed-down" space. It's quicker to take the longer route – not your straight line.'

'How amazing,' declared the Judge. 'I must say I've never come across a universe whose space behaves like that – and I've renewed quite a number in my time.'

'Huh,' said Phusis dismissively. 'That's nothing. Space can be *really* weird . . .'

On the *eighth* evening, Phusis explained that light was a wave. When you switched a lamp on, the light behaved rather like water ripples spreading out on a pond.

'So?' The Judge shrugged.

'But light travels through empty space to us from the Moon, and from the Sun and the stars,' said Phusis.

'Yes, I know that,' said the Judge. 'What of it?'

'Through *empty* space,' repeated Phusis with emphasis. 'If light is a wave, but space is empty – *what is waving?*'

The Judge was astounded. He was so taken aback he was convinced there must be some mistake. 'Look,' he insisted, 'you must have got it wrong. If light passes through empty space – as it clearly does – then it cannot possibly be a wave.'

The following *ten* evenings were taken up with Phusis having to demonstrate experiment after experiment to prove to the Judge that light really behaved like a wave. It was all very tiring for her. It meant lugging box-loads of equipment across the green from the school building to the Red Lion – lasers, slits, lenses, gratings, polaroid sheet – and then back again.

But finally her moment of triumph came.

'OK, OK,' cried the Judge. 'That's enough. You win. Light is a wave.'

Phusis grinned with relief. But then she frowned.

'What's the matter?' asked the Judge.

'Nothing, nothing,' she said hastily, then added, 'Well . . .'

The Judge waited. 'Yes? Go on. What is it?'

'Look . . . Are you sure you don't know all this stuff already? I've been thinking. There you are: this important judge from Elsewhere. You're in charge of deciding which universes will carry on and which won't. You *must* know what they're like. How can you decide properly if . . .'

'Have you any idea how many universes I have to deal with? Any idea *at all*?' he replied abruptly. 'How am I supposed to know the details? Eh? One brief look at the check-list is all I get time for.'

Phusis shrank back into her chair.

'In any case, something I've been meaning to ask *you*,' he continued. 'How come you know all these things? You're not a scientist – you just teach little kids.'

'I'll have you know, some of us teachers of little kids – as you put it – take our job seriously,' replied Phusis indignantly. 'In any case, I haven't told you anything that wasn't known *years* ago.'

'Oh.'

They sat glaring at each other.

Eventually the Judge resumed, 'This light of yours, it's a wave, OK? But it still manages – somehow – to wave itself through empty space.'

Phusis nodded.

'Fascinating,' he said.

'Yes,' agreed Phusis. 'Fascinating. And so many different kinds of light,' she added casually, as she packed up the last of the equipment.

'*Different* kinds of light, did you say?' murmured the Judge . . .

On the *nineteenth* evening Phusis passed white light from the desk lamp through a prism of glass. Immediately the light blazed forth in all the glorious colours of the rainbow.

'Good gracious!' exclaimed the Judge. 'Where did they come from?'

'Magic, isn't it?' said Phusis. 'White light. Common-or-garden white light is actually made up of all those brilliant colours.'

'But how?' asked the Judge, clearly perplexed.

'Different wavelengths,' explained Phusis. 'Light is a wave, right – a wave made up of humps and dips. The distance between any two humps or any two dips is called the *wavelength* . . .'

'Yes, yes,' said the Judge impatiently.

'Well, white light is a mixture of waves of different wavelengths; the prism separates them out. Red has a longer wavelength than orange; orange is longer than yellow; and so on – through to violet.'

'How odd,' said the Judge. 'There was I thinking if something was white, then it wasn't coloured. But you're saying white is *all* the colours.'

She nodded.

'And it's just a difference in wavelength that gives the light its different colour?'

'That's right,' she said. 'But that's just a start. You'd never guess what happens if you make the wavelength of light longer than that of red light. In fact,' she laughed, 'it's the very *last* thing you would expect light, of all things, to do . . .'

On the *twentieth* evening, Phusis went on to explain. 'Light is all about seeing things – making things visible, right?'

'Yes.'

'The strange thing is that if you stretch out its

wavelength to be longer than that of red light – it becomes *invisible*!'

'*Invisible*!' exclaimed the Judge. 'How can *light* be *invisible*? You mean – it's not there any longer?'

'Oh, no. It's there all right. You can detect that it's there – with equipment. But you can't see it, not with your eyes.'

'But what's the point of it?' sneered the Judge. 'I can't imagine anything more useless than light you can't see.'

'Ah, but it's not useless,' she said. 'What we're talking about is *infra-red* radiation – or "heat rays". As we sit by this fire here,' she said, pointing to the flames licking up the chimney, 'it's the infra-red radiation that warms us. It's the same with the warmth we get from the Sun. Infra-red radiation. We couldn't live without it.'

On the following nights, Phusis went on to talk about longer wavelengths still. These were microwaves – radiation to cook by in microwave ovens. Microwaves come to the Earth from outer space. These tell us how the world was originally created in a violent Big Bang. Phusis explained how the waves were given out at that time, and ever since have wandered the universe. Microwaves are also used for radar. You send them out, they bounce off distant objects, and come back to you again. If you know how long they took to do the return journey, you can work out how far they've been – how far away the object is. It's another way of 'seeing'. It's how bats 'see' when they fly in the dark.

At yet longer wavelengths, there are waves used to carry TV signals. 'Odd, don't you think, that waves that are themselves invisible, can be used for producing visible pictures on our TV screens,' she remarked.

Then come radio waves – short wave, medium wave, and long wave. These carry a different sort of message; they allow voices to be heard over great distances.

'But what of light at *short* wavelengths?' asked the Judge. 'Is there any light with wavelengths less than that of violet light?'

'Oh yes,' replied Phusis. 'But again it's invisible. Ultraviolet light it's called. It's what gives us a suntan. Funny that: it has no colour of its own – being invisible – and yet it can change the colour of your skin.'

Later, she went on to talk of shorter wavelengths still: X-rays that can penetrate your body and allow doctors to take a look inside you.

Together Phusis and the Judge spent many a pleasant evening exploring all the wonderfully varied things light could do under its various disguises.

Then, on the *fifty-first* evening . . .

Peep! Peep! . . . *Peep! Peep!* . . .

'Excuse me one moment,' said the Judge, pulling out his portable videophone. A small screen popped up on which Phusis could just make out the picture of a dwarf-like creature. He had pointed ears and great big shiny eyes. He looked very eager and bouncy.

'Yes, Fred. What is it?' asked the Judge.

'Ah. That's you, is it, sir? Good. Er . . . Well . . . I was just wondering what was going on, like. Seeing as how I haven't heard anything from you for . . . well, for some time, sir. Everything all right?'

'Yes. Yes, everything's fine,' said the Judge.

'Good. Er . . . Right, well, just thought I'd let you know the Schlurpit's all ready and raring to go. It's been in for its 1,000-universe service – like I said it was due for. Retuning of the gargulator, fresh set of teeth for the cruncher-squirt, that sort of thing. Nicely warmed up – purring as sweet as can be. So, er . . . Just waiting for you to give the word, like.'

'Yes, thank you, Fred. I'm just about to leave here.'

'So, tomorrow then?' said Fred rubbing his hands.

'Yes. It looks very much like tomorrow. I'll let you know as soon as I get back.'

'Great! See you.'

The Judge folded away the videophone and returned it to his pocket. 'You heard that?' he asked Phusis.

She nodded.

'All good things come to an end,' he said. 'I believe that's one of your sayings.'

She smiled.

'Yes, if you don't mind, I think I should start my packing,' he said.

'Of course,' agreed Phusis. 'Mind you, it's a shame . . .'

'Phusis. No,' he interrupted, shaking his head. 'Not again.'

Phusis blushed. 'Sorry, sir. But it *is* a fascinating

world. At least *I* think so. I can't help it if I have this urge to share . . .'

'I know, I know. Yes, I must say I've begun to take quite an interest in your quaint "olde worlde" world. But as you heard, there's work to be done. So, Phusis, I'm afraid this definitely is Goodbye.'

2   *What's the Matter?*

As E-Day (Extermination Day) kept getting post-
poned, people tried as best they could to carry on as
normal. But the threat was always hanging over
them, and did have its effects. Greengrocers, for
example, were having a hard time of it. No longer
were parents able to persuade their children to eat up
their greens 'or you won't grow up strong and
healthy'; the children knew they weren't going to
grow up anyway. Sweet shops, on the other hand,
thrived. ('But, Mum, there won't be time for my teeth
to drop out.') Talking of teeth, dentists were idle as
patients phoned in to postpone their appointments –
for ever. Teachers could not get children to study for
exams that would not now take place. Insurance
companies boomed – then went bust. (At first, lots of
people rushed to insure themselves against early
death. Then they realized this was not going to work.
Not only that: Who would be around to pay out after
E-Day – and to whom? There followed a rush to take
out the money again.)

Even the younger children at Phusis's school knew
by now that something was up. They had heard of
the 'Man from Elsewhere' who could hide himself
behind a hologram. So they set to and drew pictures

of what they thought he might really look like – anything between Father Christmas and a dinosaur.

It was while they were doing this that Phusis was called to the telephone.

'Phusis? I was wondering if you could come over,' said a deep, croaky voice. She didn't recognize it.

'Sorry. Who is that?' she asked.

'It's me – the Judge.'

'The Judge?' said Phusis, not quite believing it. 'But it doesn't sound a bit like you. Have you changed your voice as well as your appearance now? And where are you speaking from? I thought . . .'

'I'm still at the Red Lion, and I'm not feeling very well,' he said, sounding very sorry for himself.

'Why? What's the matter?' she asked.

'How should I know?' he growled crossly. 'I asked the landlord, but he's just a raving lunatic. Went on about it all being due to my spending the night *flying!*'

'*Flying!*' exclaimed Phusis. 'What . . .? Where have you been flying . . .?'

'I *haven't* been flying,' he snapped. 'But he kept on insisting: "You have flew." The idiot!'

Phusis laughed. 'Not F-L-E-W; F-L-U! You have influenza.'

'What's that? Oh forget it. *I'm not well!*'

'No, no. I'm sure,' said Phusis hastily. 'It would be most unwise of you to go out for the next few days. You ought to stay in the warm and have lots of hot drinks.'

She agreed to come over and see him after school,

adding, 'You will, of course, remember to give Fred a call. We don't want him . . . you know . . . Not with you still here.'

So it was on the *fifty-second* evening, Phusis again made her way over to the Red Lion, this time carrying bottles of linctus and cough sweets. As she did so she recalled that she had often wondered what the point of flu viruses was. But perhaps this was it: all along they had been meant for this moment in time – to save the world – until the end of the week at any rate.

The Judge was sitting in his dressing gown and slippers in front of the fire when she arrived. She began showing him the pictures the children had done of him. He roared with laughter – only to end up coughing. She gave him spoonfuls of medicine.

'Right,' he said, once he had recovered. 'Anything more you want to tell me about this world of yours? Might as well, seeing as how I'm stuck here.'

'Well, let me think,' said Phusis. 'We've talked about light – its many disguises; light the great messenger – telling us about the world. So . . . Yes, why don't we ask: What's out there in the world? What kind of matter is giving out the light?'

'OK. Fire ahead,' said the Judge, sucking a cough sweet.

'How many different kinds of material would you say there were in this world? Any idea?'

'Different kinds?' he murmured, 'Lots. That's one thing I noticed on the check-list before coming. You have lots of different materials: brick, cement, plaster, coal, wood, paper, steel, glass, plastics, straw, cotton, air, water, cardboard, leather. How many more do you want? There must be hundreds ... Thousands?'

'Several hundred thousand,' declared Phusis. 'And those are just the ones we know about – the ones that have been listed so far. Hundreds of thousands of them.'

'So?' he said casually.

'Ah, but do you know how many basic elements they're made up from?'

He shook his head.

'Ninety-two,' she said.

'Ninety-two?' he repeated. 'You're saying ... I don't believe it. You're saying you start off with just ninety-two different kinds of thing – *elements* did you call them? And from ninety-two, you make hundreds of thousands of different ...?'

'That's right.'

'No kidding? Most universes have vast, vast numbers of basic building blocks. A real headache trying to keep track of them all. But you say ...' The Judge shook his head. He found this very hard to swallow.

Over the next few weeks he had Phusis coming over every night armed with bottles of chemicals and jars of powders. Together they would mix them to see what new chemicals they could produce. The landlord complained bitterly to his friends. (He never dared face the Judge himself.) The smells that wafted out from under the door of the saloon bar were vile; they made your eyes water. Also, the Judge was rather clumsy and kept spilling nasty liquids all over the table top and burning holes in the carpet. To Phusis's alarm, he kept muddling up his medicines with these chemicals. Then there were the numerous explosions that frightened the customers in the other bar. And that's to say nothing of the night of the fire – the one that almost burned the place down.

The Judge's attack of flu had long since cured itself. But so interested had he become in the experiments, he had not noticed. Needless to say, Phusis did nothing to draw his attention to this. Instead, she continued to produce medicines and to suggest more and more experiments – each one more strange and unexpected than the last.

'Today I take hydrogen – a gas that burns fiercely – and oxygen, which is what you need for a fire.'

The Judge looked worried.

'We combine these two dangerous elements . . .'

By now the Judge was halfway towards the door.

'And lo and behold: *Water!*' declared Phusis.

The Judge was thunderstruck. 'But water puts fires *out*!' he exclaimed. 'How on . . . (Dammit, where are we?) How on *Earth*, did that happen?'

On another occasion she took sodium – which earlier the Judge had seen burning and fizzing and spitting in a most frightening manner when put into water – and combined it with a nasty gas called chlorine (the yukky smell you get in swimming baths). The Judge still had his fingers in his ears when she produced the end result: *Salt!* Plain ordinary salt, which Phusis then calmly spread on to the take-away fish and chips she had brought with her.

*

But despite the great success of all these experiments, the Judge eventually began to show signs that the novelty was wearing off.

So, on the *112th* evening Phusis told him about atoms.

'The ninety-two elements are made up of atoms. Each element has its own kind of atom. For example, it takes two atoms of hydrogen stuck to one of oxygen to get water; one atom of sodium stuck to one of chlorine gives salt. But what's an atom made of?' she asked.

He shrugged. 'Tell me.'

'A tiny particle called a *nucleus*, and even tinier particles called *electrons*. (Remember the electrons? They were the ones trying to break the World Speed Record.) Right well, the electrons buzz around the nucleus like bees round a hive. The nucleus is made up of particles called *neutrons* and *protons*. So, there we have it. The ninety-two elements are made of electrons, neutrons and protons. That's all: just *three* different things. Neat, eh!'

'*Three?*' he exclaimed. 'It's not ninety-two different things. It's really only *three*?'

'Yes, I'll show you . . .' Phusis said.

Over the following nights, Phusis brought her videodisc player, and the Judge experimented with various schemes for combining neutrons, protons and electrons. Gradually she convinced him: it really was possible to build this richly varied universe from just three types of basic building block.

*

The 130*th* evening: Phusis revealed one of the world's greatest mysteries: every electron is identical to every other electron. They are more identical than any pair of 'identical' twins ever born; they are *absolutely* identical. The same goes for neutrons; they too are all identical to each other. The protons also; there's no way to tell them apart.

'But how do they manage it?' asked the Judge.

Phusis shook her head. 'No one has any idea. Scientists have not begun to answer that question; perhaps they never will.'

The next night, she told him that a proton weighed about 1,836 times as much as an electron; the neutron a little bit more. Why 1,836? What was so special about that number? Again, scientists have no answer.

On successive nights the mysteries came thick and fast.

Each proton carries a small quantity of electricity; each electron carries *exactly* the same amount, but of an opposite sort – what we call *negative* rather than *positive* electricity. The result is that when we have an atom with as many protons in the nucleus as there are electrons buzzing around outside – which is how atoms normally are – the two types of electricity cancel out precisely. Is there some special reason for this?

'Well?' asked the Judge.

Phusis shook her head. 'No idea. No one has a clue.'

An electron seems to have no size. Though we think of it as a particle – a tiny, tiny pebble-like thing –

in fact, when one looks closely at it, there's no 'outer surface' to be seen, and hence no 'inside'. It appears to be point-like.

'How curious,' observed the Judge.

'That's why we think it doesn't make any sense to ask what an electron is made of,' said Phusis. 'You can hardly think of even more basic building blocks stuck together – in some arrangement or other – if the arrangement doesn't take up any space!'

'And is that the same with protons and neutrons?' asked the Judge.

'Oh no,' replied Phusis. 'They've got a definite size.'

'So, what are *they* made of?'

'*Quarks!*' declared Phusis with a grin.

'Sorry? What was that?'

'Quarks,' repeated Phusis.

'Oh.'

'Odd sort of name, I know. But it's not my fault; no one asked me what to call them,' Phusis laughed. 'Anyway, you're now going to ask me what quarks are made of,' she continued.

Actually he wasn't. He had grown restless and had begun glancing at the clock on the wall over the fireplace. Phusis recognized the danger signals: he was beginning to get bored. She thought she had better hurry it up, when she caught sight of the Judge's hand – or at least, her attention was drawn to where the Judge's hand *ought* to have been. She screamed!

'What . . . What . . .?' she cried, pointing to the end of his left arm – an arm that just ended in mid-air!

The Judge looked down. 'Oh, I say. I *am* sorry,' he apologised. 'You must think me very rude.'

With that, his hand materialized, and all looked normal again. Phusis stared at it speechless, holding her tummy as if she were about to be sick.

'The hologram,' explained the Judge. 'It's just the hologram. It takes on the shape of whatever form of life . . . But we've been into all that. I'm sorry, I must have been day-dreaming – not concentrating on what you . . . Look, it won't happen again.'

Phusis gradually recovered. 'Sorry,' she said at last. 'I wasn't expecting anything like that. I keep forgetting this is just a . . . a hologram.' She gave a nervous laugh.

'Yes, well, it is. You mustn't take any notice,' he said. 'Now, where were we? You were about to tell me what these quarks of yours are made of?'

'Er . . . Well no, I wasn't.'

'Oh. But I thought . . .'

'No. Quarks are like electrons. That's what I was about to say. Quarks seem to be point-like – so, again there's no sense in asking what they're made of.'

'Ah. So that wraps it up then,' said the Judge. 'Hmmm. Very satisfactory. Quarks and electrons – both of them point-like – nothing more to say.'

'Ah, but there is,' said Phusis hurriedly. 'Quarks are so friendly. You wouldn't believe it . . .'

'Friendly? What do you mean? How can . . .?'

'But they are. They always go around together. You never see a quark on its own. They go around in threes. Three quarks make a proton; three make a neutron.'

'But you must see a quark on its own *some* of the time,' said the Judge.

'No. Never.'

'Well, knock one out. Take a proton and bang it until one breaks off.'

'Scientists have tried – but it can't be done. That big machine for making electrons go fast – that two-mile "gun barrel" we were talking about – it's been fired at protons.'

'Well?'

Phusis shrugged. 'Didn't harm the protons at all. The bullet electrons just bounced off. The three quarks were still hanging on to each other.'

'You're sure the quarks are in there? There couldn't be some mistake . . .?'

'Oh they're there all right; they can be seen.'

'Well then, hit them with something heavier. You did say electrons were the *lightest* particles; try something more beefy . . .'

'It's been tried. There are machines for accelerating protons – great big circular machines, miles in diameter. But it's no good. Even when the quarks are hit by a proton, they still stick together. It now looks as if we shall *never, ever* be able to separate them.'

'How very strange,' remarked the Judge. He chewed thoughtfully on his pipe. 'The proton bullets just bounce off, eh?'

'Er . . . Well not exactly,' said Phusis, with a mischievous glint in her eye. 'When protons collide at very high energy, something absolutely incredible happens.'

'Oh, what's that?' asked the Judge, beginning to take a fresh interest.

'New particles suddenly appear!'

'The quarks *do* pop out, you mean?'

'No, not that. No. *New* particles are created – particles that were not there before. You start off with two particles – the bullet proton and the target proton – that's what you have *before* the collision. Then *after* the collision, you still have the two protons you began with, *plus* the extra particles.'

'But where did they come from?' demanded the Judge. 'You can't just create things – not from *nothing*. It's not allowed. Only the Federation of Universes can decide that. All creation and all . . . renewal is subject to Federal permission.'

'Of course. Quite right,' agreed Phusis. 'The new particles don't come from nothing.'

'Oh? Well, where do they come from? Sounds to me as if something very irregular is going on here.'

'No, no,' laughed Phusis. 'It's all above board. The particles come from energy.'

'Energy?'

'Yes. All that energy the bullet particle brings with it. Some of it goes to create the new matter.'

'But how?' asked the Judge. 'What's energy got to do with matter?'

'Matter *is* energy – a frozen kind of energy. All the matter around us is frozen energy. That chair you're sitting on; if that energy could be released it would be like letting off a gigantic nuclear bomb!'

The Judge looked down at the chair and shifted uneasily.

'It's all right,' Phusis assured him with a giggle. 'It's all under control. Nothing to be alarmed about. It's *frozen*. It won't get out.'

'Are you sure?' asked the Judge.

She nodded. 'That sort of energy gets out only very rarely,' she continued. 'Like when a nuclear bomb is set off – and even then only a tiny fraction of it gets out.'

The Judge still looked a little anxious.

Phusis smiled. 'Amazing, don't you think, that all these boring, ordinary, objects around us are actually packed with explosive energy?'

'Very interesting. So, tell me more about these new particles . . .'

'Ah, yes. In the collisions – between the protons – some of the energy gets frozen into new particles. It goes both ways, you see. In a bomb, some of the frozen energy in matter gets released; in the collisions, some of the energy of movement of the bullet proton gets frozen.'

'And what are these new particles?' asked the Judge. 'More protons . . .?'

'No, no. At least . . . *sometimes* a new proton is produced, but more often you get entirely new types of particle: one that is 273 times as heavy as an electron, another 940 times . . .'

'*Any* weight, yes?'

'No. That's the curious thing. 273 – *not* 272 or 274. Always 273. If you want to produce something different, then you have to go all the way up to another allowed value – 940 for instance.'

'But why? Why not any weight?'

'No one really knows. It's like the weight of a proton: always 1,836 times the weight of the electron – why?'

And so it was that, beginning on the *152nd* night, Phusis began to describe all the weird kinds of particles that have been discovered in the collisions – together with their weird properties. Yes, they have properties that ordinary protons and neutrons and electrons don't have – properties with odd names like *strangeness*, *charm* and *beauty*.

Some are weirder than others. Take the neutrino, for example. What a slippery customer he turns out to be!

'Suppose you took a neutrino and shot it into the ground,' said Phusis. 'How far down do you think it'd go? A centimetre? A metre? The odds are it would come sailing out on the other side of the Earth! At this very minute, as you sit here, millions of neutrinos are pouring down from outer space and passing right through your body – and you can't feel a thing!'

The Judge looked down at himself, half expecting to see himself riddled with tiny bullet holes – but everything looked in order.

'And another thing about neutrinos,' she continued on another occasion, 'they spin – rather like the Earth spins on its axis. Now that in itself is nothing special; lots of particles do that. But neutrinos *always* spin the same way. Their spin axis is always accurately lined up with whatever direction they are going in – and they always spin left-handedly (the opposite to the way the normal right-handed corkscrew goes as you twist it into the cork).'

'Why?' demanded the Judge.

Phusis could only shrug.

Then later she was to tell him about *anti*protons. In certain ways these are like protons. For example, they weigh exactly the same as a proton. But in other ways they are the opposite. Their electric charge, for instance, is negative, whereas with the normal proton, as we have already noted, it is positive. There are also *anti*electrons; these have properties opposite to the electron. When a particle meets up with its antiparticle, they cancel each other out! They disappear – explode – releasing their pent-up frozen energy.

This gives rise to the thought that perhaps there might be stars and planets out there in outer space that are entirely made of antimatter: antielectrons buzzing around antinuclei made of antiprotons and antineutrons. If so, the antipeople living there would live perfectly normal lives just like we do. In those worlds the only ordinary matter they would ever come across would be the rare example of it they could produce in their high-energy collisions between antiprotons. The only way we could discover whether they were made of ordinary matter like ours or antimatter would be to ask a brave astronaut of ours to go there and shake hands with one of them. If they promptly blew up, then we would know the answer!

*

'But, going back to the way new particles are made in the collisions,' said the Judge on the 251st night. 'How do you decide which particles you're going to make in each collision?'

'You can't,' declared Phusis. 'There's no way of telling in advance what any one collision will give you. You just have to wait and see.'

'But that *can't* be right,' he claimed.

'But it *is*,' she insisted. 'You know what particles you start with – the two colliding protons. You also know what you end up with – the new particles. What you *don't* see is the actual moment of collision. Just before? Yes. Just after? Yes. But the actual collision itself? No. The actual moment when it all happens is something cloaked in mystery. It's beyond our control. We cannot make particles to order. It's all a matter of luck.'

'I don't like the sound of that . . .'

Peep! . . . Peep! . . .

'. . . nor of *that*,' he added with a sigh.

Most evenings they would get interrupted by calls from Fred. This was no exception.

'But, sir, it's not good to leave the Schlurpit idle all this time. It's the same with any machine; the parts seize up. Much better to keep it running. So, how about it? If you can't let me have this universe yet, is there some other I can be getting on with? It doesn't have to be anything special. A tiny, tiny, universe – no life – third class – that sort of thing. Just something to keep the Schlurpit running and in good nick, like?'

The Judge laughed. 'Oh Fred, ever the one for getting on with the job. No you can't practise on another universe – not even a little one. You know the rules . . .'

'But . . .' protested Fred.

'Stop your worrying,' the Judge interrupted. 'You'll get your universe – *this* one. We're just about finished down here now.'

'Oh, boy! That's great, sir,' yelled Fred, his eyes lighting up.

Phusis's heart sank.

3 *Nothing Is What It Seems*

'This *won't* hurt,' insisted Phusis.

'But what is it?' asked the Judge.

'A plaster. That's all. A sticking plaster. It'll keep the dirt out. You can't be too careful – even if it is only a scratch.'

Phusis stuck the plaster firmly on to the end of his thumb.

'*Only* a scratch, you say. So it's not important. There's no need for me to change my plans about leaving today.'

'Leaving? Er . . .' Phusis thought fast. 'Well, you can leave if you want. Certainly. Chances are you'll be OK. But . . .' She slowly shook her head.

'But what?' he asked anxiously.

'Oh nothing. It's just that . . . well, with scratches and bites from dogs you never can tell. Some people have been known to die from them.'

'Die?' exclaimed the Judge, looking horrified.

'Oh, it's rare. The dog has to be suffering from rabies – a disease dogs sometimes get. But the doctors at Elsewhere will know all about that; they'll be able to deal with it . . . yes?' she added mischievously.

'Well . . . I don't know.'

'Oh. Well, if you're not sure. Not *absolutely* sure
. . . it might be best to stay on for another day or
two. That way, if anything nasty does develop we
can get someone – an experienced doctor who
knows about such things – to look after you. No
point in destroying the universe – and all its anti-
rabies drugs – just when you might be needing
some.'

The Judge stared hard at Phusis. Was she exag-
gerating . . .?

'Actually, I still don't understand what happened,' she continued. 'Toby is such a friendly dog.
He's lived here at the pub for years. He's never done
anything like this before. And you say he just wandered into the room and *attacked* you? You didn't
provoke him?'

The Judge looked a little uncomfortable.

'It's not that I provoked him. It's just that . . . it
was the hologram – this,' he said pointing to himself. 'It's the new *automatic* model.'

'Automatic? Sorry. What . . .?'

'Yes, automatic. Normally you have to set the
hologram manually – to take on the shape of the
life-form you're dealing with. But this is the latest
model. It can sense what the life-form is, and set the
hologram automatically. That's how it happened.
The dog came in; I reached down to stroke it. And
. . . Well, there you are.'

'Sorry. I still don't quite under . . .'

'I turned into a dog – I mean the hologram made
me *look* like a dog. That's when the wretched thing
attacked me.'

'Well, I'm not surprised,' declared Phusis indignantly. 'Poor Toby. You must have given him the shock of his life.'

'Yes, yes, well . . . It can't be helped. In future I'll have to keep an eye on things and use the "Manual override" switch to keep it on "human being".'

There was a pause.

'In future?' murmured Phusis. 'Um . . . Do I take it . . .?'

'A *few* days. Just a few more days. Well, as I see it, there's no point in taking unnecessary risks. Rabies, you called it?'

'Very wise,' said Phusis.

'That's enough,' he said sternly. 'I've told you before: I am not one of your children. I don't need to be told when I've been "a good little boy".'

Phusis blushed. 'Sorry,' she mumbled.

'OK. Go ahead,' he said abruptly, as he sat down in his usual chair. 'Amuse me. I'm sure you've got something else up your sleeve to tell me about this world of yours.'

She smiled. 'Well, as a matter of fact, I was telling the children about space today.'

'Space? We've done that. Light going in bent paths; gravity and all that.'

'No I wasn't thinking about that. Something else.'

'Well you can't keep on about empty space. Come on now; it's *nothing*. How much more is there to say about *nothing*?'

'Who said it was nothing? It's chock-a-block. Full of interesting things. Fields, for instance.'

The Judge frowned. He turned and looked out of

the rear window – the one facing the rolling country-side stretching beyond the back yard of the inn. Phusis followed his glance – and burst out laughing. 'Not *those* sorts of fields, silly . . .'

He glared at her angrily.

'Er . . . I mean . . . *sir*,' she mumbled. 'Sorry . . . I meant . . .'

He ignored her apology. 'What sort?' he demanded crossly.

'It's hard to say,' she said. 'I suppose the best way of describing it is to say that it's a kind of *strain* set up in space.'

'A *strain*?'

'Yes. An invisible strain. You see, when you have an object like the Moon, even though it's a quarter of a million miles from the Earth, it's able to sense that the Earth is there – even though there's no direct contact between them.'

'Gravity, you mean,' said the Judge.

'That's right. The Earth's gravity affects the space around it – puts a kind of strain into it – so when you place another object, the Moon, into that space, it feels the strain. The strain tells the Moon that something heavy – the Earth – is over here. It doesn't have to be in contact with the Earth itself; they don't need to be touching. It just feels the strained space; that's enough.'

'But what about these "fields" you were talking about; what are they?' asked the Judge.

'That's what I'm talking about: the strain in space is the "gravitational field" of the Earth. That's what we call it: a *field*.'

*

This conversation took place on the 252nd evening. Over the next few nights Phusis spoke of other types of strain that can occur in space. She dangled a length of cotton six inches in front of the face of the TV set in the bar, and switched the set on. The cotton immediately shot towards the set and flattened itself on the screen. The Judge was fascinated. Phusis explained that inside the TV tube, a beam of electrons was hitting the screen. The electrons brought with them their negative electricity. This, when smeared over the face of the screen, set up a field that stretched out into space in front of the set – this time an electric field. That was what drew the cotton to the screen.

They went on next to play with magnets and compass needles. Again objects were able to affect each other across seemingly empty space; this time it was all due to magnetic fields.

Phusis later described how if you took an electric charge and moved it about, the electric strain in the surrounding space moved with it. This changing pattern of strain showed up as a ripple moving out into space away from the charge.

'Any idea what that ripple is?' she asked.

The Judge shook his head.

'Light!' she announced.

'Light?' repeated the Judge. 'Sorry . . . How can . . .?'

'That's what light is made of: ripples of electric and magnetic fields. And not just light. Radio waves, and X-rays, and all the other disguises light takes on – they're all ripples. So, for example, you want to send out a radio wave? What do you do? You make electrons go up and down a piece of wire – a wire called

an aerial. That sends out a ripple of strain in space:
the radio wave – a ripple of changing electric and
magnetic fields.'

'I see,' murmured the Judge, stroking his chin
thoughtfully. 'Very interesting. But I still don't
understand . . .'

Peep! . . . Peep! . . .

'Not now, Fred,' said the Judge.

'Yes, sir. But do you realize . . .'

'Some other time, Fred.'

'But what about my wife and . . .'

The Judge snapped the little screen down, and
replaced the videophone in his pocket.

'Strains in *what*, precisely?' he continued, as if
nothing had happened. 'That's what I don't understand. It's all very well saying there are these strains
in space, but if empty space is really *empty*, there's
nothing there to strain.'

Phusis smiled. 'I'm sorry,' she said. 'When I said
the space was "empty", I meant there weren't any
lumps of matter there; we're talking about the space
in between the lumps – in between the stars and the
planets.'

'Yes?'

'But that's not to say there isn't *anything* in that
space. It's *packed* with stuff. That's the trouble.
There's so much of it, you can't see it.'

The Judge drummed his fingers impatiently on the
table. He gave Phusis a black look. Was she playing a
joke on him? he wondered.

'It's like this,' she said. 'Well, a *bit* like this: here we
are in this room surrounded by space. There are

objects: you, me, the table, the chairs, and all the other things. In between the objects is empty space . . .'

'No there's not,' interrupted the Judge. 'There's air.'

'Exactly, but how do you *know* there's air there?'

'It's obvious,' he spluttered.

He thought for a moment, then filled his lungs, leant forward and blew hard. The ash from the ashtray went everywhere. 'Oops!' he exclaimed. 'Sorry. Didn't expect . . . Here. Let me.' He helped brush her down.

'Anyway,' he continued, once they had settled down again. 'As I said: it's obvious.'

'Ye-es,' agreed Phusis. 'It's obvious if you disturb the air – if you squash it up in your cheeks, and push it from here to there. But suppose we sit quite still, stop breathing for a moment – just a moment. Suppose we leave the air undisturbed – evenly spread out through space. Is it obvious then that it's there?'

The Judge thought for a moment, then shrugged.

'It's not, right?' continued Phusis. 'And what if we were dealing with a different kind of gas – one that was spread out evenly throughout all of space – and I mean *all* of space – I mean the space *inside* objects (you, and me, and the table and chairs) as well as the space outside them and between them – that would be *really* difficult to detect, yes?'

The Judge lit up his pipe, and pondered for a while before nodding.

'So. There you are then!' declared Phusis

triumphantly. 'That's what space is like. It behaves a bit like that gas. It's actually chock-a-block full of stuff – but it doesn't look like it, because it's spread out evenly; there's the same amount of it everywhere.'

'But if you can't detect this stuff, what's the point of it?' demanded the Judge, clearly irritated by the whole idea.

'Ah, but you *can* detect it – by disturbing it. It's only hidden from us when it's evenly spread out – like the air. If you disturb the air – by blowing it – then you can show that it's there. Same with space; disturb its evenness, and it shows up.'

'But how do you do that . . .?'

Peep! . . . Peep!

'Look, sir, I really must talk to you,' came this worried voice.

'I'm in the middle of something, Fred.'

'But what about the wife and kids?'

'What about them?' demanded the Judge crossly.

'Well, it's the mortgage. We're going to be out on the street if this goes on much longer. I'm behind on the payments, see. I need the overtime. I can't keep up the payments without the regular overtime. And what with all this nothing-to-do lark, my take-home pay . . . well, I mean to say – you know, when we were schlurping universes by the . . .'

'Another time, Fred. Not now.'

'But . . .'

'DON'T MAKE ME REPEAT MYSELF.'

Again the Judge slammed down the little screen, and pocketed the videophone.

'Where were we?' he said angrily.

'Er . . . Ah, yes . . . How do we disturb space?' she reminded him.

'Exactly. How do we do that?'

'You knock a hole in it!' she declared.

For a while the Judge sat there not knowing whether to laugh or what. 'You knock a hole in it,' he repeated, mockingly. 'You knock a hole in empty space.'

'Yes.'

'Oh, come on!' he exclaimed. 'Pull the other leg. Er . . . You do have a saying about pulling legs, don't you?'

Phusis smiled. 'Yes, we do. But I'm being perfectly serious,' she assured him. Looking around her, she continued. 'As we sit here, we're surrounded by a sea of protons.'

'We're *what*?'

'They're everywhere, evenly spread out, part of the invisible stuff of space. There they are, each one with the properties of a proton. Now, suppose we were to remove one – suppose we were to knock it out of that sea. What would be left?'

'What would be *left*?' repeated the Judge. 'How should I know? This is nonsense.'

'No, go on,' insisted Phusis. 'What would be left if you knocked a proton out of the sea?'

The Judge folded his arms and did not reply. He just glared at her.

'You'd have a hole,' said Phusis calmly. 'An *absence* of a proton. Something that had all the *opposite* properties of a proton . . . Think about that . . . What is something that has all the opposite properties of a proton?'

'Opp . . .?' The Judge thought for a moment. 'You mean . . .'

Phusis nodded. 'An *anti*proton. Quite. That's what an antiproton is. It's a hole in that sea of protons. It's where one of those protons used to be. And because we see the hole in the stuff of space, we know that the stuff itself must be there.'

The Judge's brow became wrinkled. 'I do believe you're serious.'

'Of course I am,' she said. 'I wouldn't waste your time . . .'

'But I thought you said earlier there were other antiparticles – antielectrons.'

'Antielectrons, antineutrons, antineutrinos,' said Phusis. 'Yes, they each have their antiparticles, and yes, they are also holes in space.'

'So, there's a sea of neutrons in space?' suggested the Judge. 'Is that what you're saying?'

'And one of electrons, and one of neutrinos. I told you: empty space is chock-a-block full of stuff!' she laughed.

'Well I never. I can't say I've ever come across anything remotely like this before. In all other universes when they talk of "empty space", that's what they mean: it's *empty*!'

As night succeeded night, Phusis spoke of other ways in which the evenness of space could be disturbed. For example, a negative electric charge tries to push other negative charges away from it, and attracts positive charges towards it. (It's the attracting force between the negative charges on the electrons and the positive charge on the nucleus that keeps them together in an atom.) These forces don't just take place between the particles we can see; they also affect the particles of the invisible sea that makes up space. So the charge on an electron will tend to push away the charges on the electrons belonging to the sea. This disturbance can be detected.

The evenness of space can also be disturbed by gravity. Phusis had already spoken of the way light travels more slowly through the strained, warped, space close to a heavy object like the Sun. Now she explained how this warping of space is responsible for the curved orbits of planets, and why balls and stones thrown up into the air fall down to Earth again.

'In fact,' said Phusis one evening, 'this warping can get so severe, you get a black hole!'

'A black hole? You mean an antiparticle?' said the Judge.

'No, no,' replied Phusis. 'Not that kind of hole. Actually, I suppose they shouldn't be called "holes" at all. They're regions of space where gravity is so strong that anything straying into that area is sucked in. It can't ever get out. Not even light is fast enough to get away.'

'So what happens to them – when they get trapped in the black hole?' asked the Judge.

'They get crushed out of existence,' declared Phusis.

'They *what*?' he exclaimed.

'That's right. Everything gets squashed down to a

point at the very centre of the hole.'

'A *point*?'

She nodded.

'And what happens to it then?'

She shrugged. 'No idea. Some people think that it all gets squirted out into some other universe – somehow – but that's just a guess. There's probably no way of finding out.'

'Hmmm,' observed the Judge. 'There was that universe with the white holes . . .'

'Sorry?'

'Oh, just a universe I had to deal with. It had these points where matter kept pouring out. No one had any idea where it was all coming from. I suppose the stuff could have been coming from yours.'

'How exciting!' exclaimed Phusis.

'No, on second thoughts, I shouldn't think so,' continued the Judge. 'That universe doesn't exist any more.'

On a later evening the Judge remarked, 'You remember how we got into all this? I blew, and all that ash went over you. Remember?'

Phusis nodded.

'Does the stuff of space ever do that – push things around, I mean?' he asked.

Phusis explained that in the far reaches of outer space, the stars are gathered together into great swirling bunches called galaxies. Our own Sun is a star and also belongs to a galaxy.

'But I was forgetting,' she said, suddenly becoming embarrassed. 'You know this already. You've actually been round our universe and seen all this for yourself. Sorry.'

'That's all right,' he said. 'Carry on.'

'Well, on your travels, did you notice anything peculiar about the galaxies – the way they were moving?'

'Moving?' asked the Judge looking puzzled.

'The way they were all moving away from each other?'

He shook his head. 'I can't say I did . . .'

'But you *must* have. It's one of the most important things about our universe . . .'

'Well, I didn't, all right?' snapped the Judge angrily. 'I was tired at the time – having to listen to all those whining complaints from everyone. Besides, it was ages ago. How can I be expected to remember . . .'

He glanced at the calendar on his wrist watch. He frowned. 'Good grief!' he exclaimed. 'That can't be right. That means . . . I must have been here . . . According to this, the Inquiry ended *two hundred and seventy* days ago! I don't believe it. No wonder Fred's been getting into a state . . .'

'270? Is that what you said? 270,' she repeated, trying to look surprised. 'My, my, how time flies.'

'Flies? No, I don't have flu. I got over that ages ago.' The Judge made as if to get up.

'But don't you want to know the answer?' asked Phusis.

'Answer? What?'

'Space . . . pushing things around.'

'Oh . . . Very well. Get on with it. But be quick. I

really must start thinking about packing.'

'The answer is yes,' said Phusis hurriedly. She was alarmed. The Judge seemed suddenly to have lost all interest. The whole of the right leg of his hologram had disappeared.

'Space does push and pull things around,' she continued. 'That's what's happening to the galaxies. All the galaxies are moving away from each other. The further away any galaxy is, the faster it's rushing off into the distance. They aren't rushing away from each other through space – not *through* space. It's space itself that's expanding. The very space itself – empty space – it's getting bigger. And as it gets bigger, it carries the galaxies along with it.'

The Judge found this hard to take in. 'Empty space – gets bigger? How . . .?'

'I'll show you tomorrow.'

'No you WON'T!' thundered the Judge. 'You'll show me *now*.'

'But I can't. I need a rubber sheet.'

'Then get one. Look, I'm not having you wasting any more of my time. You've just heard me say it's been 270 . . .'

'But I have to stick pennies on it.'

'Pennies!'

'And there's not time for the glue to dry.'

So it was that Phusis turned up the following night with a roll of rubber sheeting under her arm. She was not sure whether the Judge would still be there. She was relieved to hear from the landlord that he had not yet left. However, she was disturbed to see a row

of packed suitcases in the hall, all bearing the label
'ELSEWHERE'.

'It works a treat,' she said to the Judge on entering
the saloon bar. 'I've been showing it to my children
this afternoon.'

She unrolled the sheet and showed him the pennies she had stuck to it. 'These represent the galaxies,' she said. 'Now, if you get hold of that side, I'll
hold it here. That's the way. When I give the word we
both pull, right? OK. Got a firm grip? Right, then
pull!'

With that they pulled the sheet in opposite directions
to stretch the rubber. As they did so, the pennies
separated further and further from each other.

'There!' declared Phusis. 'See what I mean? It's the
stretching rubber – the expanding space between the
pennies – that carries them along. And that's how it
works with the galaxies; expanding space pulls them
along.'

'Ah,' said the Judge. 'Yes, I see. I get it now. Yes,
that's interesting. And this expansion – how long's it
due to go on for?'

'I'm glad you asked that,' said Phusis. 'Such an
important question. Particularly for someone in your
position.'

'Why me in particular?'

'Well, you having to decide the future of the universe, and all that. No one could expect you to make a
decision without you properly considering the alter-
natives. "Renew" the universe? Yes, that's one possibility. But then again what would happen to the
universe if you decided to leave it alone? Might it be

that the universe is coming to an end anyway? What would the Federation say if you wasted their money, and your time, and Fred's time, getting rid of a universe that was due to snuff itself out?'

'Snuff *itself* out?' repeated the Judge. 'Is that a possibility?'

She nodded.

'Really?' He thought about this for a moment. Then he added, 'Well, in that case, I suppose you must be right. Never heard of a universe that might go out of existence all on its own – for *nothing*. Yes, you'd better tell me more.'

The next morning the Judge had his cases unpacked, and over the following few evenings Phusis told him how the key to the future of the universe lay with gravity. The gravity between the galaxies is slowing down the rate of the expansion. How strong is this tendency? It all depends on how much matter there is in the universe. If you work it out based on the matter we know about, then gravity will not be strong enough to halt the expansion; the universe will carry on getting bigger and bigger – for ever. But if there is more matter out there in space – matter that has not yet been discovered – who knows? Gravity might just be strong enough to stop the galaxies. What would happen then? Gravity would pull them all back together again – until they all crashed in on top of each other. The whole universe reduced to a point!

'Go on, go on,' urged the Judge excitedly. 'What happens then?'

Phusis shrugged. 'Impossible to say. That might be

the end of it – the universe wiped out. Or it might not be. It could be that everything would then bounce right back out again, and expand all over again – ready for the next bounce. This bouncing could go on for ever.'

'Fascinating,' said the Judge.

'Then, there's the question of how big the universe is; does it go on for ever? If it doesn't, what lies outside it? In fact,' she added with a twinkle in her eye, 'does that last question make any sense?'

'Make sense?' said the Judge. 'Why shouldn't it?'

'Well if you say something lies "outside" something else, you mean it's somewhere else – at some other point in space, right?'

'Yes.'

'But we're talking about the universe. That includes *all* of space. So if *all* of space is inside our universe – if space is part of the universe itself – there can't be any of that space *outside*. And if there is no outside to the universe, there can't very well be *anything* outside – because there'd be no place to put it!' Phusis and the Judge spent several evenings arguing about *that*!

Then came the night when the Judge remarked, 'Of course, even if you can't have anything *outside* your universe, that doesn't stop there actually *being* things other than your universe. There are all the other universes.'

'Well, sir, I just have to take your word for that.'

'Of course. When you're part of one universe, you can't expect to know anything about the others.'

'Clever that – the way *you* are able to hop from one to another, and go to Elsewhere.'

He nodded. 'Yes, it's clever.'

'But if they're not *outside* this universe – these other universes – where . . . well, you know . . .'

'They have their *own* types of "space", that's how,' smiled the Judge. 'There's more than one type of "space". That's why they don't have to be anywhere in *yours*.'

'Oh I see . . .' murmured Phusis. Another idea was taking shape in her mind – yet another way of keeping the conversation going, and delaying his departure once more. 'I suppose it must be a bit like the way things are in this universe: lots of different spaces – not just one,' she remarked, trying to sound casual.

'I beg your pardon,' said the Judge. 'Diff . . .?'

'Of course. You don't think there's only *one* do you?'

'Nobody told me about this!' he exploded. 'More than one . . . Oh no, don't say there are yet more forms of life I've got to consult stuck out . . .'

'No, no . . .'

Peep! . . . Peep!

'For goodness' sake, not now, Fred.'

'But, sir,' wailed the Exterminator. 'Have you heard the news? I'm to be put on half-pay. *Half-pay*! I can't manage on *that*! They say my productivity has dropped. Well, I ask you: whose fault's that? I've tried telling them . . .'

Snap! The Judge stuffed the videophone under a cushion.

He turned back to Phusis. 'Go on. More spaces? What kinds of spaces?'

'Er . . . Yes,' mumbled Phusis. These sudden reminders of the threat hanging over the universe did nothing for her concentration.

'Yes, I was saying that there are different spaces. As we both sit here we occupy the same space. But if I do this . . .' She got up and started walking slowly towards the door. 'Then my space is no longer your space.'

'Don't be ridiculous,' exclaimed the Judge. 'Of course it's the same.'

'No it's not,' she claimed, still continuing her slow walk. 'If we had the same space, it would mean that we would agree how far I am from that door – our measured distances would be the same.'

'Yes, yes. Of course. So?'

'But they aren't. The distances aren't the same. If you measured it with your ruler, and I measured it at the same moment with a ruler I was carrying with me, we would get different answers.'

'Then get better rulers,' said the Judge. 'Rulers of the same length.'

'No, it's nothing to do with that,' she replied. 'The rulers are identical.'

By now she had reached the door. She stopped, and came back to her seat.

'I don't get it,' he said helplessly.

'It's what I say. If I'm moving – moving relative to you and to this room – then my space is not your space. The distances I measure in this room – measuring them along the direction I'm going in – they're not the same as yours; my distances are squashed up. At any moment, the distance to the door is shorter for me than it is for you.'

'You're saying that if I measure the distance to the door as I am now – not moving; let's say I get 20 feet, right. And then I get up and start moving towards the door, and measure the distance again – straightaway, before I've had a chance to walk any distance – you're saying the door will be *closer*? I might only get . . . 10 feet, say?'

Phusis laughed. 'Yes, that's right,' she said. 'But it wouldn't be 10 feet. You could only reduce a distance of 20 feet down to 10 if you were travelling at something like 9/10ths the speed of light – about 160,000 miles per second. No, at walking pace, or at any other speed you're likely to get on Earth – the speed of a train or an aircraft – the squashing up isn't noticeable. But it's there; it's always there. Given the right equipment, it can be measured.'

The Judge was stunned. For several evenings they did nothing but use the videodisc player, to try out how things would be if one flew around at different speeds up to – or at least *almost* up to – the speed of light. How they laughed when they realized that, to an astronaut flying at such speeds, the Earth, the Moon and the Sun would all seem to be squashed flat like pancakes.

Meanwhile, from time to time, a muffled *Peep!* . . . *Peep!* could be heard coming from under the cushion.

4   *Time Marches On – Or Does It?*

With the future of the universe at stake, you'd have thought that world attention would be focussed on the talks at the Red Lion. For a short while it was. When the Judge did not go home as expected, the media people returned to Bumbledon in force. There was a flood of newspaper articles about Phusis: how to pronounce her name; what might be in the large bag she always took with her; what clothes she was wearing; etc. There was one very unkind article about 'Miss Fussy'. That upset her very much.

Meanwhile, the politicians tried to outdo each other with claims that the credit for the stay of execution was all theirs. They declared that the advice they had given Phusis was playing a vital part in the negotiations. (What advice?! What negotiations?! Phusis fumed to herself.)

But as quickly as interest had revived, it died again. For one thing, pop singers and film stars were announcing the most unlikely marriages. They competed with each other to see who could set up the silliest wedding. It was good publicity. And with the end of the world coming, it was not as though they would have to stay married for long. The papers lapped it up.

Then there was the World Cup. At first, it was cancelled – along with everything else. Footballers stopped training. But with each new postponement of the Judge's departure, fresh hopes were raised. Now there was a mad rush to fit in one last competition before E-Day. Excitement was at fever pitch: the opening games were shown on all TV channels. (Well, perhaps not *all* channels, but it certainly seemed like it.)

Thus, Bumbledon again returned to normal. As far as the media were concerned: 'End of the World? Forget it. Yesterday's story; it's not *news* anymore.'

So it was on the *312th* evening, Phusis was able to walk in peace to the Inn. As she did, she realized she was running out of interesting things to say to the Judge about the effect high speed had on space. If she was to carry on playing for time she would again have to rack her brains and think of something new. And tonight she was especially tired. It was Friday – the end of a week in which the children had all got very excited. Jamie, for example, had spent days rushing up and down the corridor; 'But, Miss Phusis, it's an *experiment*. I'm making the door at the end come closer. And *you* said we have to go very, very, very fast to see anything!' Then there were the projects – pictures of astronauts and models of spacecraft – every one of which, the children insisted, Phusis had to take to show the Judge; 'And tell us what he says.'

In fact, the Judge spent quite a long time patiently examining the children's work. He even took the trouble to write helpful comments on each.

'The children will be ever so pleased,' said Phusis. 'You seem to like doing this. I take it you have children of your own?'

He smiled. It was the smile of someone enjoying a private joke. 'Er . . . Not exactly. No, where I come from, people like me don't have children – not the way you have them. There are *other* ways.' He gestured in a vague sort of way. He paused; then shook his head. 'No, I can't explain; it'd take too long – and we don't have the time,' he added, looking across at her knowingly.

Phusis was almost too tired to argue with him. But not to keep arguing . . .

'Depends,' she said.

'Umm? Depends? What depends?'

'Depends whose time we're talking about.'

'*Whose* time? What do you mean . . .?'

She looked at him with a broad smile. 'Oh come on,' she said. 'I know when you're having me on.'

'Having you . . .? What . . .?'

'You know as well as I do, there's more than one time. There *has* to be more than one time. All that stuff we've just done on what speed does to space. Right then . . . It's obvious.'

'Obvious?' said the Judge, looking flustered.

'Well, yes. It's obvious time must be affected by speed too. You *must* know that,' continued Phusis. 'You can't destroy the world without knowing *when* it happens! What are you going to write in your records? You do keep records . . .?'

'Of course, we do,' he muttered crossly. 'Every form in twenty copies.'

'So, what are you going to put down as the time at which the universe was destroyed? *Your* time, or . . .' At this point she rose from her seat and slowly started walking towards the door. '. . . or *my* time?'

'Oh,' groaned the Judge. 'You're not going walk-abouts again are you?'

She resumed her seat. 'Just making my point.'

'What point?'

'If I'm moving, my time is not the same as yours. Just as we don't share the same space, we don't share the same time.'

The Judge slowly shook his head. 'This I do not believe.'

'But I'm afraid you *have* to,' she said. She looked about her, then sighed. 'Oh no. The videodisc player. I haven't got it with me. I knew this morning I'd be needing it . . .' The tears began to well up. 'Sorry,' she mumbled. 'I'm . . . I'm tired. I forgot . . . That Jamie – I could kill him sometimes.'

'No need for that,' said the Judge. 'You can safely leave me to deal with him – and all the others.'

He laughed. It was too much for Phusis; she burst into tears. She sobbed and sobbed.

'I'm sorry,' cried the Judge. 'Didn't mean it. Joke. Joke, yes? It was just a joke – sort of. Here . . . this any good?'

He offered her a handkerchief. She took it and wiped her eyes.

'Oh dear. What must you think?' Phusis sighed.

'That's all right,' said the Judge. 'My fault. I . . . I wasn't thinking. Come, let's call it a day.'

'But . . .' Phusis protested.

'No need to worry. You'll get your chance tomorrow. Tell me all about it tomorrow. I'll wait. I can't very well go without knowing how I'm to fill in the forms, eh?' he chuckled.

Having spent most of Saturday morning asleep, Phusis felt much better by the time she reached the bar that evening. 'Right,' she said, setting up her videodisc player. 'Take a look at this. Here's our astronaut again. He's flying to a distant planet – just like last time. He works out the distance to the planet, and let's say it's half what the mission controller says it is. His space is squashed up by the speed, right?'

The Judge nodded.

'Same on his journey back; again he thinks the distance is half its normal value.'

'Yes, yes,' said the Judge a little impatiently.

'Right now, suppose when he sets out they set their watches to the same time, and then when he gets back they compare them again. What are they going to find?'

'Go on,' he said suspiciously.

'Their watches won't agree any more,' she replied.

'So? Stop buying cheap watches.'

Phusis smiled. 'No, no. It's not that. The watches haven't gone wrong. They just don't agree.'

The Judge looked cross. 'Look . . . What are you on about?'

'It's simple really,' Phusis assured him. 'The astronaut thinks he's going half the normal distance, right? So. If he goes half the distance, he takes half the time. When he gets back, his watch won't read the same as the mission controller's one. If the controller says he's been away for 20 years, the astronaut says it took only 10 years.'

'Yes, but he knows it's not *really* 10 years,' said the Judge. 'He'll see his watch going slow during the flight. He'll know it's screwed up – because of the speed.'

'But he won't,' said Phusis.

'Won't what?'

'He won't see his watch going slow.'

'Of course he will – if you tell him to keep an eye on it,' protested the Judge.

'No, you don't understand,' explained Phusis patiently. 'It's not that the speed screws up the workings of the watch, or anything like that. It's *time itself* that's slowed down in the spacecraft. *Everything* is slowed down in the spacecraft: the rate at which the TV monitor pictures are scanned on the control panel, the rate at which the lights wink on and off, how fast the light bulbs burn out, the astronaut's heart beat, his breathing – and his thinking. So he's looking at a slow clock with a slow brain. The clock's slowed down to half its normal rate, but the brain is also slowed down to half its normal rate. That means the watch looks perfectly normal to the astronaut.'

'I don't believe this,' said the Judge.

'But it's true,' declared Phusis. 'We *know* it's true. It's all been tested out.'

'But who is right?' he demanded. 'Whose time is the *real* time?'

Phusis laughed. 'They're *both* real. That's the point. There's no reason to say one is more real than the other.'

*

Over the next few nights, with the help of the videodisc player, they experimented with astronauts flying at different speeds. It was like watching slow motion replays on television. The Judge marvelled at how much things could be slowed down. Right up very, very close to the speed of light, things almost came to a complete standstill.

'At this rate the astronaut could live for ever!' he exclaimed.

'Certainly. That's exactly what the controller thinks is happening to the astronaut,' Phusis agreed. 'But that's not how the astronaut sees himself. As far as he is concerned, life carries on as normal. Remember, his thinking is slowed down.'

On the 325*th* night, Phusis revealed a second way in which time was affected. If the controller said two things happened at the same time – let's say, a lightning flash in Manchester and another in Los Angeles – then according to the astronaut, they would *not* happen at the same time! One would happen *before* the other. For example, the Manchester one might happen a split second before the Los Angeles one. If there were another astronaut, flying in the opposite direction to the first, he would also claim that the lightning flashes did not happen at the same time. But, according to this astronaut, they happened in the *opposite* order to what the first one found; the Los Angeles flash occurs first!

The Judge leant forward holding his head. 'That's enough. I don't think I can take any more.

Different spaces, different times. IT DOESN'T MAKE ANY SENSE!'

Phusis smiled triumphantly. 'Ah, but it does,' she announced. 'This is a mystery we *do* understand – to some extent, anyway. Tomorrow evening? Same time?'

Without looking up, and still clasping his head, he nodded wearily.

The 326*th* day: Phusis prepared to introduce the Judge to the Fourth Dimension. She had tried the idea out on her children first; they thought it was 'absolutely brill!'

That evening when she met the Judge, she produced from her bag a camera. It was one of those instant Polaroid ones. She proceeded to take photographs of the clock on the mantelpiece. She did this from different angles. In no time the pictures were ready. These she set out in a row before the Judge.

'There you are,' she said. 'All different!'

'So?' said the Judge.

'But they all look *different*,' she said. 'Doesn't that worry you?'

'Why should it?'

'But you were worried about the distance to a planet being different for the astronaut and the mission controller – and about the Earth looking squashed up to the astronaut . . .'

'That's not the same,' he interrupted. 'Those were *real* distances. These don't show real distances. They're just . . . photographs.'

'What's wrong with photographs?' asked Phusis.

'Well, for a start, they're *flat*! *Real* objects – that clock there – that's not flat. It's solid. You can look at it from different angles. Its shape changes. I mean: the shape *appears* to change. But it's not *really* changing – just its *appearance*. That's all these photos show: just the *appearance* of the clock – from some particular angle or other.'

'Quite!' said Phusis, her face beaming. 'That's what I'm saying. The clock – the real clock – is three-dimensional; it's 3-D. That means it spreads out in three directions: up-and-down, left-and-right, and backwards-and-forwards. The photo has only two dimensions: up-and-down, and left-and-right; it can't see what's happening in the forwards-and-backwards direction. That's why the photograph is just an appearance; we call it a 2-D "projection".'

'Yes, yes,' said the Judge, 'I know all that. What's your point?'

'Well,' smiled Phusis. 'We're used to photos looking different because we know that they're just 2-D projections of something that is actually 3-D – the clock. So, what I say is this: if we find that even 3-D objects can look different – the distance to a planet or the shape of the Earth – might that not be because they are just projections too? Mere appearances – not the real thing itself?'

'Appearances?!' said the Judge, puzzled. 'How? They're three-dimensional . . .'

'Yes, 3-D. But suppose – just suppose – that the *real* object had even more dimensions. Suppose it had *four*! You could then get 3-D projections of something that was 4-D. That way these projections wouldn't

79

have to look the same. They could be different, depending on your point of view. Depending on your speed.'

The Judge looked lost.

'In the case of the clock,' continued Phusis, 'if you want different photos, you have to walk round it – change the angle – look at it from different sides. Well, in 4-D, if you want a different kind of "angle" on things, you do it by changing your speed. The astronaut and mission controller – they've got different speeds so they have different "angles".'

He scratched his head. 'But I still don't get it. This fourth dimension . . . I mean . . . *Where* is it? I don't see any fourth dimension. And you can stop grinning like that,' he added crossly. 'If you're so clever, point to it. Come on, let's see it.'

Phusis went across to the fireplace, reached up towards the mantelpiece, and tapped the top of the clock.

The Judge looked across at her. 'What's that supposed to mean?'

'That's it: the fourth dimension. TIME. That's where it is.'

'*Time!*' he exclaimed. 'How can *time* have anything to do with it?'

Phusis thought for a moment, then resumed. 'Take the astronaut; he flies to the distant planet, right? OK, now fix your attention on two events: first, his departure from the Earth; second, his arrival at the planet. Now, we've already seen that the astronaut and the controller see things differently. They don't agree about how far it is to the planet; in other words, they don't agree how far apart the two events are in space. They also don't agree about the time of the journey; they don't agree how far apart the two events are in time. Now why's that? It's all because space (3-D space) is just an appearance, and time is also just an appearance. What is *real* is four-dimensional – a kind of "space" made up of ordinary 3-D space, *plus* a fourth dimension that's all to do with time. It's called 4-D "spacetime".'

'But I don't see the point of it,' said the Judge. 'Why get so complicated?'

'But it's not – not really,' said Phusis excitedly. 'You see, the astronaut and the controller may not agree about their 3-D projection in space, or about their 1-D projection in time, but they *do* agree about what exists in 4-D spacetime. If you ask them: What is the separation between our two events in *four* dimensions? They get exactly the same answer!'

'The *same* answer?' repeated the Judge.

'Yes. Brilliant, eh!'

'Oh . . . Oh, I see . . .' he murmured. 'If they get the *same* answer in 4-D . . . OK, fair enough. Yes, I can see that begins to make a bit of sense, I suppose.'

'Yes, good old Einstein!'

'Who?'

'Oh nothing. Just someone who used to live here once. It was Einstein who first discovered all this.'

'Ah.'

'So, that's how we know the world is 4-D,' said Phusis.

'Hmmm,' nodded the Judge. 'Very interesting.'

'Mind you, it took a long time to work it all out –

time being so different from space – measuring one with rulers, the other with clocks,' she laughed.

Over the course of the next few nights, they explored the possibility that there might be yet more dimensions: a fifth, a sixth, a seventh, etc. – dimensions that haven't been recognized yet because they too, like time, don't at first seem to have much in common with ordinary space.

Then came the *365th* evening – an evening Phusis would never forget. She had had a lovely day. Lots of nice letters from all over the world con-gratulating her on having saved the world for a whole year. She had baked the children a large anniversary cake. They wanted her to take a piece to the Judge – but she thought it wise not to.

She arrived at the Inn at the usual time. 'Good evening!' she called out cheerily to the landlord, and went straight to the saloon bar. The next moment there was this terrible scream. The door to the bar was flung open, and Phusis ran out. She knocked the landlord flying in her panic, and fled down the passage towards the exit. The landlord had hardly picked himself up, when he was again flattened – this time by the Judge.

'Phusis! Phusis!' the Judge yelled. 'It's *me*! Come back. Phusis! Stop!' He ran after her.

The landlord painfully got to his feet and, swearing under his breath, brushed himself down. Frowning darkly, he made his way down the pas-sage to the saloon bar. He peered cautiously in through the door. Everything looked perfectly

normal. He shook his head.

'And him a judge and all that,' he muttered. 'Right disgusting, if you ask me. Should jolly well know better. He's old enough to be her father . . .'

With that he hurried off to the public bar – to spread a few rumours.

Ten minutes later, the Judge had managed to persuade Phusis to return.

'But it was *horrible*! A monster!' she declared. 'Lots of heads. I'm not kidding. LOTS. And it was sitting right there where you are. Slumped over it was, all the heads lolling about, eyes shut. It looked asleep.'

'Yes, I was asleep – dozing, at any rate,' said the Judge.

'You? You mean upstairs – in your bedroom? Yes, I was wondering where you were. I certainly hadn't expected to meet up with *that*.' She gave a little shiver. 'I wonder where it's got to. You don't think . . .?'

'It's *here*,' he said, pointing to himself. 'I'm the monster. It was me.'

'But . . . It couldn't . . .' protested Phusis. 'It didn't look a bit like you. Those heads . . .'

'I was asleep. I was dreaming. I was dreaming about the ten-headed parallel processors of Pollux. They were the ones I visited just before coming here to Earth. In my dream I was arguing with them. So . . .'

He shrugged.

'So what?' she asked.

'So the hologram made me look like one of them. It must have thought they were real. It's an automatic hologram, remember? Brand new model – not tried out before.' He added with a laugh. 'I suppose we should put it down to teething troubles, eh? But it'll be OK; I'll tell them when I get back. They'll think of something – to stop it happening again.'

'And do they really look like that?' asked Phusis. '*Ten* heads, did you say?'

He nodded.

'How did they get that way?'

'Evolution,' replied the Judge casually. 'It's how evolution happened to go on Pollux. Two heads are better than one, right? Do your thinking twice as fast as anyone else. Big advantage in the struggle for survival. Then three heads are better than two – and that's how it goes. So far they're up to ten. Mind you, they're in trouble now.'

'Why's that?'

'Equal rights. They've just passed a bill in the Pollux Parliament; all heads have equal rights. Before any decision is made now, there has to be a vote. The population's been going down ever since.'

Phusis looked blank. 'Why . . .?'

'T-junctions. Coming up to a T-junction you have to decide – turn left, turn right? They now have to hold a ballot. If the result happens to come out 5–5: straight ahead.' He shook his head. 'Nasty. Touch and go whether they wipe themselves out before they develop the eleventh head.'

'The eleventh?'

'Odd number. Breaks the deadlock.'

The Judge lit up his pipe. 'Anyway, enough of that. Anything more you want to tell me about this 4-D spacetime of yours?'

'Not really. Except . . .'

'Mmmm?'

'Well, now we know space and time are all bound up together, it does make you wonder just how similar they are to each other. Take, for example, the fact that all space exists at each point in time. No problem about that – right? All of space; all this space around us exists *now* – at this instant of time, and at every other instant – yes?'

He nodded.

'Right then, if time is just another dimension, you'd expect that all of time would exist at each point of space.'

Again he nodded. But then immediately frowned. 'All of . . .? Say that again. All of *time* . . .?'

Phusis smiled. 'Exactly. Odd, isn't it? To think that at this point in space – right here in this bar – all the past (everything that has ever happened in this room) and all the future (whatever is going to happen here later on) – it all exists, along with us sitting here in the present.'

The following night she went on to explain that, in a sense, nothing ever *happens* in spacetime; nothing ever changes.

'You see, if things change, they must change *in time*. But spacetime cannot change in time – because spacetime is not *in* time at all. It can't be. Time is *part* of spacetime itself. Time is in spacetime, not spacetime in time. It's the other way round, see?'

'I think so,' murmured the Judge, puffing away on his pipe. 'I must say it's not easy thinking of time as just another dimension of space.'

'Ah . . .' said Phusis uncertainly. 'No, that's not *quite* right. Certainly time is much more like space than we used to think; that's very true; but there are still differences between space and time – important differences.'

'Oh? Go on.'

'Ummm. I'm afraid that will have to wait for tomorrow. I need a video.'

'A video, eh? I like videos.'

On the 367*th* evening, as promised, Phusis played him a video cassette. It began with a girl in a swim suit mounting the steps to the top diving board. She walked to the very edge of the board and stopped. Raising her arms, she prepared to dive. But Phusis pressed the 'Pause' button; and the girl froze in mid-action.

'OK,' said Phusis. 'Which way is she facing?'

'Facing? She's facing the water,' replied the Judge. 'At least, I hope for her sake she is,' he added with a grin.

'No, I didn't mean that,' said Phusis. 'Which way? Is she facing North, South, East, West, or what?'

'How should I know?' he grumbled.

'Quite. There's no way of telling. That's how space is. One direction is as good as another. Now watch.'

She pressed the 'Pause' button a second time, setting the video running again. The girl dived; there was a splash; she disappeared into the water.

'That's one way of showing the video,' she said. 'But there is another.'

As they watched, circular ripples on the water's surface slowly shrank towards a central point; splashes of water rose into the air and swiftly came down together at the same central point; at the same time the girl came shooting out of the water, feet first! As her fingers emerged, the surface of the water suddenly went completely calm; the girl meanwhile soared gracefully through the air, and landed neatly on the edge of the board; she lowered her arms and proceeded to walk backwards to the steps; she did not look where she was going, but got there safely; finally, she went down the steps, backwards.

The Judge chuckled. 'I always get a laugh out of that,' he said. 'Films going backwards, videos going backwards – they look so ridiculous.'

'Oh,' said Phusis innocently. 'You could tell?'

'Tell what?'

'You could tell the video was going backwards.'

'Of course.'

'Well, there you are then. There *is* a difference between space and time. You knew which was "forward" and which was "backward" – you could tell the direction of time; but you couldn't tell the direction in space – which was "North" and which was "South".'

'Ah,' said the Judge. 'So that's the difference – between time and space.'

Phusis sat there looking quietly amused.

'What's so funny?' he asked suspiciously.

'Nothing, nothing,' she shrugged.

'Come on,' he insisted. 'What's the joke?'

'Well . . . You know how everything's made up of

atoms – including everything we see there on the video – the swimming bath, the girl . . .'

'Ye-es.'

'Right. Well, let me show you what's happening at the atomic level – what's happening to the individual atoms.'

She put the tape on 'Fast forward' for a while; then again on 'Play'.

'A short piece of animation,' she announced. 'This is the first thing atoms do . . .'

They watched as two atoms vibrated back and forth. That's all they did: back and forth, back and forth. It was as though the atoms were tied to the ends of an invisible spring.

'So?' said the Judge.

'OK,' said Phusis. 'They can vibrate. Now let me show you this.'

She pressed the button labelled 'Review'. They watched as again the atoms vibrated back and forth. After a while, the Judge said irritably, 'We've seen this. Can't we get on . . .'

'No we haven't; not really. This is different,' she replied. 'The video's going *backwards* now.'

'Backwards?'

'Yes. Why? Couldn't you tell?'

The Judge looked. 'No,' he shrugged. 'Should I? It looks the same to me.'

'Quite. Vibrating atoms don't look any different whether you're looking at them going forward in time, or backwards. Now look at this. This is the second thing atoms can do.'

They watched as one atom entered the picture

from the left, and another from the right. They met at the middle of the screen, and bounced off – one going straight up out of the top of the picture, the other in the opposite direction out of the bottom.

'Now let me show that the other way,' suggested Phusis.

This time the atoms entered top and bottom, bounced off each other, and went out left and right.

'I can tell that was going backwards,' said the Judge.

'How?'

'Obvious. That time they came in from the top. The first time . . .'

'But which way round showed the *actual* way it happened?'

'Eh?'

'Is there anything to stop two atoms coming into view from the top and the bottom of a picture, and going out sideways? Do they *always* have to come in from the left and right?' she asked.

'Well, no. They don't *have* to,' he agreed.

'So if I told you that in point of fact I showed the backwards version *first*, and the correct way round *second* – could you tell?' she challenged.

'Well . . . I suppose not . . .'

'Because that's what I did!'

He scowled. 'Look, what's this got to do with anything?'

'Well, I'm just telling you: that's all atoms ever do; they vibrate and bang into each other. That's all that's going on in that swimming bath.'

'So?'

90

'But atoms vibrating and banging into each other –
you can't tell which way the video ought to be
shown, right? Either way looks OK. So, how come
you stick together a whole lot of things – none of
which tells you what the correct direction of time is –
and you end up with a complete video where it's
obvious what the direction of time should be?'

The Judge was dumbfounded.

'For the complete video, one way looks OK,' she
continued. 'The other looks . . . How did you put it?
Looks "ridiculous" . . . was that it?'

'I don't get it,' he declared.

'Another thing,' said Phusis. 'The reverse way of
playing a video shows something that *can* happen –
it's not impossible. It *can't* be impossible.'

'The girl coming out of the water feet first – and
landing on the board?' jeered the Judge. '*That's*
impossible. That can't happen.'

'Oh yes it can,' she assured him. 'It *must* be able to
happen. We've just said everything is made of atoms;
and atoms only ever do things that can happen either
way round. So, if the atoms make up a girl diving off
a board into water, it stands to reason – by simply
reversing the movement of each atom – you'd get a
girl shooting up out of the water and landing on the
diving board.'

'But HOW?' thundered the Judge.

'Oh, it's quite simple really,' said Phusis with a
laugh. 'The atoms in the water are all vibrating and
moving about all the time. They do it in all directions,
so it cancels out on average. But suppose – just
suppose – there was a fantastic coincidence: for one

91

brief moment they all happened to move upwards together – they all moved in the same direction at the same time. And again – just suppose – there was a girl in the water at that very spot. She'd be flung upwards by the force of the water. She'd go flying up into the air – and could land on the board.'

'Huh!' the Judge snorted. 'And what are the chances of *that*?'

'Oh, I don't know. Trillions of trillions of trillions to one against,' said Phusis. 'Certainly not much point hanging around waiting for it to happen.'

'Well, there you are,' he said smugly. 'What did I say: it's impossible.'

'But it's not,' she repeated. 'It's unlikely, yes. *Very, very, very* unlikely, I grant you. But it's not impossible. That's important. It's not impossible; it can't be.'

So it was that the Judge and Phusis spent the next 100 nights watching videos. (We did note earlier he was keen on videos!) They played them forward and backward. They argued for hours about the way in which the reverse sequence could happen. Each new sequence – from cups being dropped and smashed, to babies being born – each of them presented fresh challenges. But each time Phusis and the Judge were able to work out how the reverse sequence was indeed possible – not *likely*, but *possible*.

On the *468th* evening, Phusis began to reveal another amazing feature about time: 'We have already seen how speed can affect time,' she said. 'Well, gravity also has an effect.'

'Gravity?!' exclaimed the Judge. 'Gravity affects *time*?'

'Oh yes. Time on the top floor of a building runs faster than time on the ground floor. It's all due to gravity.'

'Good gracious. Why didn't someone warn me?' said the Judge. 'You mean I should have been resetting my watch every morning – when I came down?' He looked at his watch and compared it with the clock on the mantelpiece. 'They seem OK . . .'

'No, there's no need to worry,' Phusis chuckled. 'The effect is too small to bother about. At least, it's small here on Earth. Out there – in outer space – that's another matter. Close to a black hole . . . Wow! The effects are enormous. On the edge of a black hole, where gravity is very, very strong, it can bring time to a complete standstill.'

Several nights were spent in exploring further how gravity affected time.

Then, on the *481st* night, the Judge went back to the idea of 4-D spacetime, and in particular, how nothing ever changed in spacetime – time being part of spacetime itself.

'But things *do* seem to happen; things do change,' he said. 'Time marches on. The past is left behind; the future is yet to come. The past is over and done with; you can't do anything about it. The future? It's uncertain. There's still a chance to decide what the future will be. How does that tie up with what you were saying before – about everything being fixed – all of time existing, not just the present moment?'

Phusis replied that this was something no one really understood. It was one of the greatest of all the mysteries of this world.

And as they continued to explore this and other ideas about time, time itself continued to pass: day followed day, followed day, followed day . . .

5   *Now You See It; Now You Don't*

Peep! Peep! . . . Peep! Peep!

'I don't want to trouble you, *sir*,' said Fred. 'I know it's of no concern to you that my wife and children are about to starve. What with me not having any overtime; then it's half pay; now it's redundancy. That's right – they're threatening me with the sack. No, as I say: you're not interested in anything like that – you having much more *important* things to think about.' Fred was obviously in a huff. 'But there is something you might like to take on board: the state of the Schlurpit. I did warn you. I told you – did I not – it's got to be kept running; it's no good leaving Disposal Units idle. But what happens? Have I had any work from you? Nothing. Not a star, not a planet – not as much as a pile of potato peelings. So, what do I do? What *can* I do? I have to shut it down, right? And now – what did I tell you? Rust! That's right. RUST on my Schlurpit! So, I want it down in writing that I warned you. I gave you fair warning . . .'

The Judge had got to the point where he no longer paid any attention to Fred's calls. As the months had gone by, he had become more and more enchanted by all that Phusis had to say. He was beginning to think he had never before come across a stranger or more fascinating universe than this one.

By the 575th night, they were winding up their discussion of space and time.

'So, tell me,' said the Judge. 'Have I got this right? Space is a kind of arena, yes? A *stage* – on which everything takes place. The *actors* on this stage? They're the particles – electrons and quarks. *And* waves – we mustn't forget light waves. So, we have particles and waves moving about in space and time – except that space and time aren't separate, they actually belong to a 4-D spacetime.'

'Ye-es,' agreed Phusis uncertainly. 'Yes – and no.'

'Oh? Have I left out something?'

'Not exactly. But things aren't quite that straightforward.'

'Why not?' asked the Judge, taking a renewed interest.

'Well, you see, you talked of particles and waves as though they were different.'

'Well, they *are* different. Couldn't be *more* different. Especially your sorts of particle: the ones with no size. You did say they were point-like, remember? Well, I mean to say: try to make a wave out of that: a hump here; a dip there; then another hump; then another dip. Waves are all spread out – they have to be; can't be squashed up into a point.'

'Yes, that's true . . .' She paused and shook her head.

'What's the matter?' asked the Judge.

She thought for a moment.

'Well, take the light entering my eye, for example,' she said. 'It goes through the lens at the front of the eye. Then it hits the back of the eye – what we call the *retina*. Have you any idea what it's like to be a retina hit by light?'

The Judge shrugged. 'No. At least, I suppose . . . you get rocked up and down – as each hump and dip arrives.'

'Sounds reasonable.'

'Well, there you are then.'

'But that's not the way it is,' said Phusis. 'When scientists actually do the experiment – to find out what it's like to be hit by light – it's like being hit by a hail of bullets . . .'

'Bullets?'

'That's right: tiny, tiny bullets; gunfire.'

'Aren't you muddling things up a bit?' asked the Judge with a smile. 'We're talking about *light*, not electrons. Light is made up of waves, not particles.'

'No, I haven't forgotten,' Phusis assured him. 'When light arrives at the retina, and gives up its energy, it does it like a particle. It delivers a little bundle of energy to an electron belonging to an atom of the retina. That electron gets the energy; the electrons next to it get nothing. It's not at all what you would get with a wave. With a wave, all the electrons belonging to the retina would be set moving: up and down, up and down. As you said, they'd all get a bit of energy. But it's not like that.'

The Judge looked annoyed. 'So all that stuff you told me – whenever it was, ages ago – about light being a wave – all that was *wrong*? Is that what you're saying? Because if you are . . .'

'No, no,' Phusis hastened to say. 'It's not wrong. No, everything I said then was quite right. I'm not taking any of it back. Light does behave like a wave – *on its way to the retina*. As it goes through my spectacles, it changes direction just as you would expect a wave to do. If they were Polaroid sunglasses, the glare of the light would be cut down in just the way expected of a wave. Polaroid glasses wouldn't work if light were not a wave. And again, when the light changes direction in the lens of the eye: it's wave behaviour again. So, throughout its journey – through space and passing through objects – the light behaves as only a wave can behave. And yet, despite all that, when it actually arrives at its goal – at the very last moment – it switches to behaving like a particle.'

The Judge shook his head. He was dazed. 'I'm sorry. I can't make head nor tail of this. What are you on about? Either something is spread out (like a wave) or it's not spread out (like a particle). You can't have it both ways – and that's the end of it.'

Phusis smiled. 'If only it were,' she sighed. 'I know exactly how you feel. It's not easy. No one finds it easy. But it's true. That's how it is, no mistake about it. I find it quite maddening – especially when I have to try and explain it to others. Not that there is an explanation – not a proper one. It's simply the way things are: as light travels through space it behaves like a wave, but once it arrives it behaves like a particle.'

'Well, I don't know,' said the Judge unhappily. 'In

a way I think this is the craziest thing you have ever told me about your world.'

She nodded in agreement.

'I suppose we must be grateful it's just light that fools around like this,' said the Judge.

'Ah,' said Phusis. 'Not quite. In fact – not at all. You see, this wave/particle double act – it's not just light doing it.'

The Judge groaned.

'No,' she carried on. 'Electrons are the same.'

'What?' exploded the Judge. 'Electrons? What about electrons? You're not going to tell me they're not particles after all?'

'Er, no, no. They *are* particles – some of the time.'

'*Some* of the time?'

'Yes.'

'*When* exactly are they particles?'

'Same as with light: when they hit something; when they give up their energy. In a TV tube, say. Yes. When the electrons are travelling through the tube from the back to the front screen, they travel like waves. But the instant they hit the screen they behave like particles.'

'But if light – and now you're telling me electrons – if they've both got a wave and a particle nature, why did you tell me light was a wave and electrons were particles?'

'Ah, that's just how they happened to show up first. The scientists first came across the wave behaviour of light; that's why they called it a wave. With electrons it was the other way round – they noticed the particle behaviour first. But nowadays,' she shrugged, 'we know better. Light, electrons – in fact, everything – has to be thought of as both wave *and* particle – equally.'

'*Everything*, did I hear you say? Not just . . .'

'Afraid so,' she said gaily. 'Everything has to be treated in the same way: light, electrons, quarks, neutrons, protons, the nucleus of the atom, the atom itself.'

The Judge slowly shook his head. He was clearly not at all convinced.

That's how Phusis came to spend the following evenings doing experiment after experiment, showing him all the effects. At last, on the *600th* evening,

'All right, all right. I give in,' he declared. 'But you've got to admit,' he added defiantly, 'it's a right old muddle – a proper botch-up, if ever I saw one.'

'It's nothing of the sort!' Phusis stoutly maintained. 'If it wasn't for this wave/particle double act, the world wouldn't be anything like so interesting. It's precisely this wave/particle business that makes our universe so much more interesting than any of your other silly old universes.'

'Huh!'

'And I can prove it!'

'Go on then,' he challenged.

'Right . . . Well, then . . .' She struggled to think.

'I'm waiting,' he said, drumming his fingers.

'It's difficult to know where to start.'

'I can believe that.'

There was a pause. Then –

'Atoms never wear out!' she announced.

'Atoms *what?*'

'I told you: they never wear out. The atoms here, all around us, making up all these objects – they've been around for thousands of millions of years, but in all that time they haven't changed – not one tiny bit; they're as good as new. All that time the electrons have been buzzing around their nucleus, and they're not the least bit tired.'

'But they must have slowed down a bit. *Everything* gets worn out eventually,' the Judge protested.

'No. Not atoms. These atoms here,' she said, tapping the table in front of her, 'they're exactly the same as they were the day they were made.'

'But how?'

'Ah. You want to know their secret – the secret of eternal youth,' she said teasing him. 'Well, I'll tell you: it's the wave nature of the electrons that does it.'

'What's that got to do with anything?' he grumbled.

'Well, let's think,' said Phusis. 'We're dealing with electrons buzzing about. Not hitting anything; not giving up their energy to something else; just buzzing about. So how are we to think of the electron? Is it behaving like a wave, or like a particle?'

'How should I know?'

'Try,' she urged.

'Stop treating me like a *child!*' he warned. Then he shrugged. 'I don't know. I suppose . . . Well, I suppose – seeing as how it's not hitting anything (and hitting things is when it behaves like a particle) . . . A wave? Would it be a wave? Moving about –

through space – around the nucleus. It moves like a wave, right?'

'Yes. That's right. A wave. But not any ordinary wave: a *trapped* wave.'

'Trapped? What . . .?'

'The electron has to stay close to the nucleus; the force between the electric charges holds it there. So that means the wave can't get away; it's confined to a small region of space around the nucleus.'

'So?'

'Well, when waves are trapped, they can only wave about in certain ways: there has to be a certain fixed distance between their humps and dips – the wavelength can't be any old distance.'

The Judge looked puzzled.

'Well, I mean . . . Take a guitar: waves on a guitar string. You pluck it; what happens? Waves. You get waves moving along the string. But they're trapped; they can't go beyond the point where the string is being held down. They just bounce back and forth. But it can't be any old waves. The ends of the string can't move up and down. And that means the wave has to fit. That's the point: it has to *fit*. There has to be a fixed distance between the humps and dips to match the distance between the ends of the string. And that in turn sets the musical note – the note being given out by the guitar. It has to be that note.'

'But guitars can play any note you like,' said the Judge looking confused.

'Sure. They can play different notes. But to change the note, you have to change the distance between the humps and dips. You move your finger; you hold the string down somewhere else.'

'But what's this got to do with atoms?'

'I'm getting there,' she smiled. 'The waves on the guitar string govern the musical note; the waves belonging to electrons govern the *energy* of the electron.'

'How?'

'How?' repeated Phusis. 'No idea. It's . . . it's just the way they are, I suppose.'

'Oh.'

'Anyway. I was about to say: just as you can't sound any old note on a guitar string, you can't have any old energy for an electron in an atom.'

'Why not?'

'Well, you've only got certain waves – because they're trapped – certain allowed wavelengths. But it's the wavelength that governs the energy of the electrons. So, only certain wavelengths – only certain energies.'

The Judge nodded. 'I see. How odd. You'd have thought an electron could have had any energy it liked. But it can't, you say?'

'No. It's all been checked out – with experiments.'

'Hmmm. But tell me: what's this got to do with atoms never wearing out?'

'Ah yes. Now that's the interesting thing. With atoms "wearing out", what exactly do we mean by that? We mean the electron's energy gradually runs down, yes?'

The Judge agreed.

'But the electron's energy *can't* gradually run down,' she said. 'To do that it would have to change from its present energy – which is the value allowed by the wave – to one slightly less – which is *not* allowed by the wave. And because it's not allowed by the wave, *it can't happen*! That's why atoms can't wear out,' she concluded brightly.

'Oh,' said the Judge, looking surprised. He thought about it for a moment, then nodded slowly. 'I like it. Yes. Very clever.'

Phusis beamed. Over the next few months she went on to describe many other strange features of atoms that arise from the wave nature of their electrons: the colour of the light they emit (for example, why some street lights glow a dull red when switched on, and then a bright yellow); why atoms can combine to produce certain chemicals and not others; how electrons already in an atom stop other electrons from joining their atom; why this means there are only ninety-two basic types of atom in nature; etc.

The *685th* evening: Phusis revealed to the Judge that of all the various possible energies an electron was allowed to have in an atom, zero was not one of them. A trapped electron has to keep on the move!

'And it's not just when an electron is in an atom,' she continued. 'Put an electron in a box – like this one,' she said, picking up the match-box the Judge used when lighting his pipe, 'and it would not be able to sit still. It would be all jittery.'

'But what if you put it in very, very carefully – so that it was dead still,' suggested the Judge.

'No. It can't be done,' she claimed.

'But why not?'

'Because of its wave nature. Put the electron in the box, and you put a wave in the box. And if the wave is trapped – in the box – then only certain distances between the humps and dips are allowed, and that means only certain energies are allowed – and zero isn't one of them.'

'How strange.'

'And not just electrons. Anything that gets trapped – quarks, protons, atoms, matches . . .'

The Judge began chuckling.

'What's the matter?' she asked.

'You said *matches*!' He pointed to the match-box.

'That's right. Matches. *Everything* has a wave nature – matches, you, me. Everything is made of atoms, and atoms have a wave behaviour. So whatever they make up, it's bound to have a wave nature too. So, take these matches here. Are they just sitting there in the box doing nothing? No. They can't be. The matches' waves are trapped in there, and that means the matches can't have zero energy.'

'They've got the jitters too?' asked the Judge.

'That's right,' she said. 'And you and me.'

'What about you and me?' he asked suspiciously.

'We have our waves too. And *we're* trapped.' She pointed to the walls around them. 'And that means we can't sit absolutely still either.'

'Nor the children in your class, I dare say.'

They laughed. But their fun was short-lived. Suddenly: a mighty EXPLOSION! They were deafened. Pieces of plaster fell from the ceiling, scattering dust everywhere. The lights went out. There

was shouting and screaming coming from the other
bar.

'Quick,' commanded the Judge. 'I don't know
what that was, but we'd better get out. This way.
Hold on to me.'

Together they groped their way to the door, then
down the passage and out through the exit. People
were running out from their houses in panic.

'A bomb!' someone cried. 'It was a bomb.'

Everyone gathered on the green, children in their
pyjamas and nighties. An ambulance turned up,
siren wailing. But no one appeared to be badly
injured; just shaken and scared.

After a while, when it seemed there would not be
any further explosions, a calm gradually settled on
the little crowd.

Someone tugged at Phusis's dress. 'Please, Miss,
what was that?' It was Sarah from school; she was
pointing at the sky.

'The bang?' Phusis asked. 'I don't know. It might
have . . .'

'No, not the bang, Miss. I mean the white line up
there. The one that was up there; it's not there any
. . . No, *there* it is . . . over there now . . .'

A shooting star sped across the sky, then another,
and another. There were several all at once . . . then
dozens . . . then *hundreds*. The sky was lit up like a
firework display. That was the first sign that what
had happened was not just something special to
Bumbledon.

Over the next few days, reports came in from all
over the world: earthquakes and tidal waves on a

scale never before seen. The Grand Canyon had split wide open; instead of being 1 mile deep and 10 miles across, it was now 10 miles deep and 100 miles across. Astronomers discovered that some heavenly bodies had altered course (that explained the unusual display of shooting stars); five of Saturn's rings had become detached and were floating off into space linked together like an enormous Olympic Games logo; Mercury, the planet closest to the Sun, had plunged right into the Sun – it had completely disappeared. This caused a huge solar flare that in turn created electrical storms on Earth. These interfered so much with the reception of TV signals that the entire population of the United Kingdom missed an episode of *Coronation Street*. It was this that really brought home to people that whatever had happened, it was serious.

'Tell me, Phusis, does this sort of thing happen often?' asked the Judge.

Phusis did not reply.

'Well,' he persisted. '*Does* it?'

'You know perfectly well it doesn't,' she snapped.

He was taken aback by her manner.

'Sorry? I don't understand. Why should I . . .'

'A "rehearsal" would you call it?' she asked coldly.

'A rehearsal? What kind of . . . rehearsal?'

'For E-Day, perhaps?'

'For . . .?' The Judge sat there open-mouthed. 'My dear, you don't think for one . . .'

'What else am I to think?'

The Judge stroked his chin for a few moments.

Suddenly a thought struck him. He pulled out the videophone.

'Fred,' he called. 'Are you there, Fred?'

'Yes,' replied Fred sullenly.

'Was that you by any chance?'

'Was what me?'

'I think you know what I'm talking about.'

'Haven't a clue . . .'

'The Schlurpit,' said the Judge severely. 'Have you been doing anything with the Schlurpit recently?'

'What do you think? You tell me: what *is* there to do with the Schlurpit these days? Nothing! It's been like this for . . . how long . . . ?'

'All right, all right. I'm sorry, Fred,' apologized the Judge. 'It's just that . . . well, there's been a spot of bother down here . . .'

'A damned disgrace, if you ask me,' grumbled Fred. 'I've already told you – about the rust. I try to keep it polished, but it's a losing battle. One of these days, the whole thing is just going to fall apart, I reckon. Then what happens . . . ?'

'Polish, did you say? Have you been polishing it?' asked the Judge, his eyes narrowing.

'Of course I've been polishing it. I always do, don't I? How do you think . . . ?'

'Did you by any chance go anywhere near the button?' demanded the Judge.

'The button? What button?'

'THE BUTTON! What other button is there?'

'Oh, *that* one. Oh, I don't think so . . . except . . .'

'Yes?' stormed the Judge.

'Um . . . well . . .'

Phusis could see on the little screen that Fred was getting flustered – and was beginning to look ever so slightly guilty.

'Yes . . . well . . . I suppose there's just a . . . a possibility . . .'

'What!?'

'Well . . . er . . . it was . . . it was the rust, sir. Very rusty, it was . . . the button as well . . .'

'How many times have I told you: NOT THE BUTTON, FRED! Not without permission from me – and *certainly not with me still HERE!*'

Needless to say, the many disasters round the world, to say nothing of the unusual things going on in the cosmos, brought the threat of E-Day back in the news. But not for long. After a few days it was back to normal: pop stars, football, give-away competitions, etc. Phusis viewed all this with dismay. 'How can people be so stupid?' she asked herself. 'Filling their lives with such silliness, while at any moment . . . I've a good mind to . . .' But she stopped. It was the *707th* evening, and the Judge had asked her round once more. She thought of the children in her school. She knew that, if for no other reason, she daren't give up now. She had to keep stalling for time.

'Ah, Phusis,' greeted the Judge eagerly when she arrived. 'Sorry about all that . . . er . . . you know. Afraid we lost a bit of time there. Still, not to worry. I'm sure you can pack in a few extra "mysteries" to make up for it, eh? But before that . . .'

He sorted through some papers and pulled out a

letter. 'Know anything about this?' he asked with a half smile.

She took the letter and read:

Dear Mr Judge,
Miss Phusis says the bang was just an accident. But she's been telling us about Fred. I think Fred is very, very naughty. He frightened Nutmeg. He ought to be told off. My Mum tells me off when I am naughty.
Love and kisses
Rebecca
PS Nutmeg is my cat. She is brown.

'You mustn't hold it against her,' said Phusis, handing it back. 'They really were scared that day.'

'Yes, yes. I know,' he said. 'Here. Make sure she gets this, eh? No point my wasting a stamp.' He gave her an envelope. 'Just a little apology – sort of thing,' he murmured.

'Oh, you shouldn't have bothered . . .'

'And why not? Anyway,' he said, lighting up his pipe, 'what's on the agenda for tonight?'

Phusis popped the Judge's letter in her bag, and thought for a moment. 'Well . . . about these waves we were talking about . . .'

'Oh, not those,' interrupted the Judge. 'We've *done* those. Can't we get on to something else?'

'*Done* them?' she exclaimed. 'We've hardly started. I haven't begun to tell you the most amazing thing about them.'

'Really? But all that energy stuff . . .'

'Forget it. That's *nothing*,' she said. 'Just you listen to *this* . . .'

And with that she began to unfold the true nature of the waves. First she reminded him that the wave behaviour shows up when working out how light (or electrons or whatever) moves from one place to another. In other words, it governs where the light will land up – where it will hit – on the retina of the eye, for example. The idea is to trace the path of the waves from where they start, then through the lens of the eye, and finally on to the retina. But it's not as simple as that, she explained. The trouble is that waves, by their very nature, are spread out. This means they don't all land up at a single point on the retina; they produce a fuzzy patch.

'So? What's the problem?' asked the Judge.

'The problem is: where exactly are the particles of light going to give up their energy?'

The Judge shrugged. 'In the fuzzy patch of light, I suppose.'

'OK. If you've got lots of particles giving up their energy – which is normally the case – then, yes; pin-point bundles of energy being given up all over the fuzzy patch. But what if the beam of light is very weak? Suppose it only has enough energy for *one* bundle of energy – *one* particle. Where is *that* going to land up?'

The Judge puffed on his pipe. 'Hmmm. I guess it gets spread out, yes? Spread out over the fuzzy patch.'

'No,' she said. 'When light hits something, it *has* to behave like a particle – a point-like particle – so, no spreading out. I repeat: where *exactly* will the particle appear?'

'No idea.'

'Well, the answer is: scientists have no way of telling!'

'But . . . but they must be able to work it out – somehow.'

She shook her head. 'No. All they can say is that the particle will land up *somewhere* in the fuzzy patch. But where exactly . . .' She shrugged.

'Sorry, I don't get this. Are you saying the calculation is complicated; you need a computer – a big computer?'

'No, no. Nothing like that. No, it's something that can *never* be calculated. Nothing to do with needing computers.'

'But *why*?' he demanded.

'Well, it's all to do with the type of waves. They aren't ordinary waves – not like waves on the sea. They are waves of *probability*.'

'Of *what*?'

'Probability. They tell you the probability – or the chance – of a particle turning up somewhere. So if you look at the fuzzy patch of light, it's brighter in the centre than at the sides. That tells you – if you've got lots of particles – that more particles are arriving at the centre; that in turn means, if you've only got the one particle, the chances of it arriving there are higher. Whereas at the edges, where the brightness fades away completely, there's no chance of finding the particle there.'

'And you're saying that's *all* you can work out: just the *chances* of the particle ending up at different places?'

She nodded. 'And that goes for everything. We used to think that our world was like a huge machine. If you knew what it was doing at any one time, you could work out what it would be doing at any future time. All right, in practice that would be difficult: keeping tabs on absolutely everything – every atom. But you could *imagine* it being done. But now we know such a dream is impossible; it can't even be imagined. And it's all because of these probability waves. They govern everything – the movement of everything. That's why the future cannot *ever* be worked out. It will always remain uncertain.'

The Judge flatly refused to believe a word of this. 'You're giving in too easily,' he declared. 'There *must* be a way round this probability stuff.'

Phusis laughed. 'You're just like the scientists in the early 1900s. They couldn't believe it either. They spent years and years trying to find a way round it; trying to think up some situation where they could exactly predict what was going to happen.'

'And?'

'They failed.'

'Pah! It *must* be possible.' The Judge thought for a moment. 'Yes. That's it. It's easy.'

'Oh,' said Phusis. 'What exactly . . .?'

'An electron, right? I take a look at an electron at a certain time – let's say 12.00 a.m. – and I note where it is. I then wait a bit – until 12.05 a.m. – and have a second look. I now know how far it has gone in five minutes, so I can work out how fast it's going. So, I now know where it is – at 12.05 a.m. – and how fast it's going. So, there you are: I can now predict where it will be at any time later on.'

'But hold on,' said Phusis. 'You say you're going to "look" at the electron. How are you going to do that?'

'How do you think? I'll shine a light on it, of course.'

'You're going to bounce some light off it?'

'Yes. There's nothing wrong with that. Is there?'

'No, no,' she said. 'That's perfectly all right. But that does mean you're going to hit the electron – *hit* it, with a particle of light. And you won't know how hard you hit it. So you may be able to work out how fast the electron was travelling between 12.00 a.m. and 12.05 a.m. (from the distance and the time), but you won't know whether it's still got that speed *after* you hit it the second time. And that means you will *not* be able to predict its future.'

The Judge glared at her. He was clearly annoyed with himself; he should have thought of that. But then he brightened up. 'The energy of the particle of light. Didn't you say that depended on the wavelength – the distance between its humps and its dips?'

'That's right. The shorter the distance, the greater the energy,' she said.

A gleam came into his eye. 'And the longer the distance between the humps and dips, the smaller the energy?'

'Of course.'

'Right, well. That's it then,' declared the Judge, getting excited. 'That's what I'll use. I'll use light where the humps and dips are spread right out. That way the particles of light will have next to no energy . . .'

'Excuse me . . .'

'. . . They'll hit the electron, but they'll do it so gently, the electron won't feel a thing. It'll carry on with the same speed . . .'

'Excuse me,' interrupted Phusis. 'Are you feeling all right?'

'All right?' asked the Judge. 'Of course. Why shouldn't I be?'

'Well, it's just that you're sort of . . . glowing,' said Phusis shielding her eyes. She was right; the judge's face was shining brightly – just like a lamp!

'I am? Oh, I'm sorry. Must have been getting too worked up. Puts up the power supply to the holo-gram. Another design fault, I reckon. I'll turn it down . . .' He put his hand in his back trouser pocket. 'How's that? Any better?'

The Judge's appearance returned to normal. Phusis nodded.

'So, where was I?' he continued. 'Ah yes. Well, that's it. By hitting the electron very gently, I don't alter its speed; it carries on as before. OK?'

'Ye-es. That's OK.'

'Right, well, there you are. What did I tell . . .'

'But just a moment. What about knowing *where* the electron is at 12.05 a.m.? If you're going to predict the future you need *both* – you need its speed (that's OK; you've got that now), but you also need to know its position.'

'But I've got that too,' he protested. 'I've told you: I shine a light on it at 12.05 a.m. . . .'

'Yes, but look at the light you're using now. It's all spread out – the humps and dips. It's so spread out, when it comes bouncing back to you, you haven't a clue where it's come from!'

'What?' he exclaimed.

'That's right. If you want a precise fix on the position of the electron, there's no choice: you must use precise light – light where the humps and troughs are all neatly squashed up tightly together. But of course, the trouble with *that* is the electron then gets knocked for six.'

By now the Judge was fuming. He was determined not to be outdone. He was convinced there had to be a way round all this. So it was that he spent night after night wrestling with the problem. Each evening he would come up with yet another scheme for showing that it was indeed possible to predict the future – only for Phusis to point out something he had overlooked.

She for her part took delight in telling him all the weird and wonderful ways this uncertainty showed itself. Radioactive nuclei, for example. These are atomic nuclei that blow up like tiny bombs. The trouble is you can never tell when it's going to happen. You might have 1,000 of them, all *absolutely identical* to each other. And yet they all blow up at different times. All you can predict for any one of them is the *chance* that it will blow up after a given time.

In this way the second anniversary of their meetings came and went unnoticed – unnoticed by the

Judge, that is. Phusis knew, of course. Again she received letters from those who were grateful for all she was doing – but nothing like so many as for the first anniversary. It seemed to her that most people were now taking it for granted that the danger of E-Day had passed.

On the *840th* night, the Judge accepted defeat. He at last admitted that there must be some very deep reason why the future could not be predicted.

'Right,' said Phusis. 'Having got that sorted out – at last – now for something *really* interesting: how to make the impossible happen!'

'Eh?'

Phusis pulled from her bag a bucket. It was the one the caretaker at the school used to mop the floors with. She put it on the table, and into the bucket she placed a marble.

'OK,' she said. 'How can we get the marble out of the bucket?'

'How?' The Judge reached in and pulled it out. He handed it across to her.

'Right,' she said. 'You can lift it out. But suppose I said you were not to touch it. We had to leave it sitting in the bottom – like this?' She replaced the marble in the bucket. 'Suppose we left it completely alone; we have no contact with it at all. Can the marble get out on its own?' she asked.

'Well, of course not.'

'It would be impossible, right?'

He nodded.

'But it *can*,' said Phusis mischievously.

'How?'

'Simple. You see, the marble has its wave nature, right? And its wave nature governs where you will find it – governs the *probability* of where you will find it.'

'So?'

'So what does the wave of that marble look like? We know the marble isn't free to move about anywhere it wants; while it's in the bottom of the bucket, it's stuck; it's trapped. So the wave will be trapped.'

'Yes, yes, I know all that,' said the Judge.

'Ah, but what I haven't told you is this,' she said. 'When you work out the shape of the wave – the trapped wave – you find that most of it's in the bucket. That's what you'd expect. But the interesting thing is that a tiny, tiny, tiny bit of it spreads outside.'

'Outside?'

'Yes. Just a tiny little bit. Out here.'

She pointed to a spot on the table top just outside the bucket. 'And *that's* how impossible things can happen.'

'How do you mean?' asked the Judge.

'Well, we've just said that the marble can't get out of the bucket on its own – that would be impossible.'

He agreed.

'But the wave – the wave that governs where the marble will be – that *does* spread out beyond the bucket. And that can only mean that there is a chance – a tiny, tiny, tiny chance – that the next time you look at the marble you'll find it *outside* the bucket!'

'You mean . . . But *how*? It jumps over the top? Is that what you're saying?'

119

'Over the top? Goes *through* the wall? Who's to say? All one can say is: Now you see it in the bucket; now you don't.'

'Well, let's watch it; let's *see* what it does.'

The Judge leant forward and stared intently at the marble.

Phusis laughed. 'Not me. You can please yourself, but I've got better things to do. I said the chances are tiny; I mean *tiny-tiny-tiny*. I mean it's not going to happen for *zillions* of years. Even then you won't see it happen. One moment it will be inside; the next it will be out.'

'Oh, take it away,' he muttered crossly, pushing the bucket aside. 'Waste of time, if you ask me.'

'OK, OK,' Phusis said hastily. 'Marbles, buckets. Yes, I agree, it's of no importance – not for things like that – big things, everyday things. But when it comes to atoms and nuclei – now that's a different story. Electrons tunnelling through barriers – happens all the time. Barriers you'd think it was absolutely impossible for the electron to get through. Yet one moment it's on one side, the next it's on the other. Magic! Pure magic!'

And so it was that Phusis spent the following weeks telling of the many 'impossible' things that happen down among the atoms – all because of their weird probability waves.

6 How's That for a Bargain!

'Oh, no,' muttered Phusis. 'It's that new motorway.' She carefully wiped her shoes on the saloon bar's door mat. 'They're finishing off the work on it. The trucks come right through the High Street. Mud everywhere. You should see the state of the floors in school.' She inspected the soles and the heels. 'That's better. Got most of it off.'

As she sat down she thought the Judge looked unusually grave.

'Is anything the matter?' she asked.

'Not really,' he said. 'At least . . .'

'Yes?'

'Well, it's just that I think the time has come for us to . . .' He shrugged.

'To what?' she asked anxiously.

'Don't get me wrong, Phusis,' he said. 'I've enjoyed our chats; I've enjoyed them a lot. But . . . Well, let's face it: I've known what you've been up to; I've known all along.'

'Known what?'

'Known about the little game you've been playing.'

She said nothing.

'All these tales of yours about the mysteries of your funny old universe. Playing for time, I'd call it.

Stalling for time. The only reason I let you get away with it for so long was . . . well, as I said: I've enjoyed it. Yes. Thanks to you, I can see how your universe has a lot going for it. It's been a good universe – in its time. But that's the problem – isn't it? The sell-by date and all that.'

Phusis was staring at the ground. Without looking up, she agreed. 'Yes. It was silly of me to think I could get away with it – that I was doing anything more than putting off the evil day.' She brushed away a tear.

'Never mind,' he said. 'You did a good job, teacher.'

She looked up and smiled. 'At least, I'd like to think that in the years to come you will think fondly of this old universe, and what it was like.'

'Oh I will, don't you worry. Mind you, I'm not so sure *what* exactly I'll remember of it. You've told me so many things, my mind is in a bit of a whirl,' he laughed.

'Oh dear, I hope I haven't overdone it,' she said. Then she frowned.

'What's the matter?' he asked.

'Oh, nothing. It's just that . . . well, when I think back, I seem to have made such a mess of things – bombarding you with so many facts. I'm not surprised it's all a mad jumble for you. No,' she slowly shook her head. 'I'm afraid I'm not a very good teacher.'

'Of course you are.'

'No, I'm not. A *good* teacher would have stuck to the really important mysteries – not the details – not what this particular electron does in this particular situation. She would have stuck to the deepest mysteries – the ones that affect *everything*. That way you could have gone off with just a few clear ideas – the truly great ones. And to think I haven't even *touched* on them.'

'You *haven't*?'

'Well, no,' she said. 'Where have I ever told you about . . . well, about scientists not knowing what they're talking about? And then what about . . .?'

'*Not knowing what they're talking about?*' The Judge's mouth dropped open.

'No. Of course they don't,' she replied, as though it were obvious. 'How can they when . . .'

'Hold on. Hold on,' he interrupted. 'You're at it *again*! You're up to your little game again. I've told you: it's got to STOP!'

Phusis sank back into her seat. 'Oh dear,' she thought to herself. 'This really does look like the end.' She daren't say any more. They just sat there. She began to wonder how to break the news to her children. She thought she'd better tell the newspapers too; it was months since any of them had as much as mentioned the subject of E-Day. It seemed to Phusis that the clock on the mantelpiece was ticking louder than usual – as if it knew these were the last precious moments of the universe's 15,000 million years of history.

It was the Judge who at last broke the silence.

'A *few*, you said?'

'A few? A few what?' asked Phusis.

'You said there were a *few* great ideas.'

She nodded.

'How many – exactly?' he asked suspiciously.

She shrugged. 'Don't know. Not many.'

'How long would it take?'

'Not long.'

'Promise?'

She smiled. 'Promise.'

The Judge slowly stroked his chin. 'Well . . . I don't know . . .' he sighed.

'Would you like a drink?' asked Phusis innocently. 'I was thinking it must be my turn to order.'

He looked at her long and hard. Then broke into a laugh. 'Cheeky devil! OK. OK. You win. But let's be clear: great ideas only – and no more than a few. Got it?'

'Got it,' she said with a grin.

She went and fetched the drinks.

'Now, what was that you were saying?' asked the Judge when she returned. 'Scientists don't know what they're talking about? I can't believe that.'

'But it's true – in a sense.'

'But they *must* know. They wouldn't be able to build bridges, or make cars, if they didn't.'

'Oh yes they know how to do *that* – how to move things about; how to build things; that sort of thing. But ask them what something actually *is* – now that's a different matter. They haven't a clue.'

'How do you mean?' asked the Judge.

'Well . . . Take time. What is time?'

He shrugged. 'It's *that*,' he said, pointing to the clock.

'No,' said Phusis. 'That's how we *measure* it.

Scientists can do that all right. They can *measure* it. But what I want to know is: What actually is time itself?'

'I'm sorry, I don't see what you're driving at.'

Phusis looked about her. 'Well, take this cloth,' she said, pointing to the one on the table before them. 'I can measure it, right? I can get a ruler and measure it to be . . . ooh . . . let's say 1.3 metres long. Fair enough. But that doesn't tell me what the cloth is made of. Is it cotton, polyester, nylon, a mixture? It's the same with time. We can measure it – with the clock. We can say it's been five minutes of time since we first met this evening. But that doesn't tell me what time is made of – what the *stuff* of time is.'

'But there must be some way of saying what time is,' protested the Judge. 'Look it up in a dictionary. That'll tell you.'

'Sure. It'll tell you that time is a duration,' she replied. 'But, what is a duration? "A duration is an interval"; but what's an interval? "An interval is a span"; "A span is a period"; "A period is an epoch"; "An epoch is a while"; "A while is . . . time". And so we're back to where we started.'

'And is that really as much as you can say about it? You just go round in a circle?' he asked, beginning to take an interest.

She nodded. 'Same goes for space. What is space? "Space is distance"; "Distance is length"; "Length is separation"; "Separation is . . . space".'

'And what about other things?' asked the Judge.

'The same. Electric charge, matter, energy – everything.'

'Amazing,' he declared.

'Yes. I sometimes think it quite *creepy*. We know so much about the world – through science. That's obvious; you only have to look at what technology has achieved. But in a sense – a very deep sense – we actually don't know what we're talking about.'

'Makes you wonder what it all adds up to,' the Judge murmured.

'Nothing. It probably adds up to nothing,' Phusis said casually.

'*Nothing?*'

The next night, the 922nd, he asked her what she had meant by that remark.

'It all has to do with positives and negatives,' she said.

'How do you mean?'

'Well, take electric charge. Two kinds, yes? Positive charges on the atomic nuclei; negatives on the electrons. Now, there are lots of nuclei and lots of electrons in the world. That means there are lots of electric charges in the world. But positives and negatives cancel out, right? So, how much electric charge is there *on average*? *None!*'

'*None?*'

'That's right. It turns out there is *exactly* the same amount of positive charge in the world as there is negative. So they exactly cancel out – to give nothing!'

'How odd! What an incredible coincidence.'

'But is it? Is it just a coincidence? Or could there be some deep reason for it?'

'Such as?'

'Such as the world being made of nothing – *absolutely* nothing.'

The following night the Judge was eagerly waiting for her.

'Ha!' he said. 'This nonsense about the world being made out of nothing. Take this.' He held up an ashtray. 'Now, this isn't nothing. There's more to this than electric charge. It's matter; good solid matter. This is clearly *something* rather than *nothing*.'

'But aren't you forgetting what we learned earlier about matter? That it was a frozen type of energy.'

'So?'

'Well, energy can be positive – like it is here, frozen in the ashtray, and in the table and chairs, and so on. But it can also be negative.'

'How?'

'Whenever things are stuck together, or held by gravity forces,' she said.

The Judge looked blank. Phusis thought for a moment, then picked up the ashtray and placed it on the floor.

'There,' she said. 'That has energy, right? It has its frozen-in energy. Now I want it up here on the table. What's the problem? The problem is that it is being held down on to the floor by gravity. So, what do I do?'

She reached down and slowly lifted it up and replaced it on the table.

'There. I've pulled it up – against the force of gravity. Now, that takes energy – a bit of energy. I

127

had to give the ashtray some energy. Now we've got the ashtray up here. It looks just the same as when it was on the floor; it still has its frozen-in energy. So what's become of the energy I gave it?'

'No idea.'

'It overcame gravity. What we say is: when the ashtray was on the floor, it not only had its frozen energy – its *positive* frozen energy – it also had gravitational energy – *negative* gravitational energy. The positive energy I put into the ashtray in lifting it, went towards cancelling the negative energy.'

'Now, come on. Are you going to tell me that all the negative energy in the world cancels out all the positive? You said the amount of energy frozen into matter was *enormous* – remember?'

'So it is. But there's also an enormous amount of negative energy in the world – due to gravity. Not just ashtrays being held to floors; there is the Moon being attracted to the Earth, the Earth to the Sun, the Sun to the galaxy, our galaxy to other galaxies. There's nothing to stop all the negative energy cancelling out the positive. So again – like with electric charge – it could actually add up to nothing.'

Phusis continued over the next few nights to explain that other things also cancel out. For example, momentum. That's a property objects have when they rush about. It tells you how good they are at pushing other objects out of their way. Because on average there are as many objects going in one direction as in the opposite, all the momentum cancels out. The same applies to angular momentum. That's what objects have when they spin. But there are as many objects spinning one way as the other; the universe as a whole *isn't* spinning. So again, it all cancels out.

'How about *that!*' Phusis declared triumphantly. 'It's quite possible that the universe adds up to precisely NOTHING! A whole universe for nothing. How's that for a bargain!'

The Judge laughed. 'Well, I must say that's very clever. Can't get a universe cheaper than that, I suppose.'

'And that's not all,' she went on. 'It's not only cheap when it comes to raw materials, it's also not at all wasteful when it come to the laws, or rules, that govern the behaviour of everything.'

Starting on the 935*th* night, she began telling him what the laws were. She was right; there weren't many of them. In fact, scientists hope one day to be able to describe everything that goes on with just one single law.

Later, she went on to talk about the forces that govern all motion in the universe: electric and magnetic forces, gravity forces, forces that hold the neutrons and protons together in the nucleus, and other forces that make radioactive nuclei blow up.

'We now know the electric and magnetic forces aren't in fact different forces at all; they're just two ways of looking at the same one,' she said. 'That makes things much simpler. The same is true of the force that blows up radioactive nuclei; that is also just another disguise for electric and magnetic forces. So, it makes you think, doesn't it? Could it be that there is actually only *one* type of force? All the forces we're used to are just different disguises of the one single force? One force, one law. Wouldn't that be BRILLIANT?'

'That would certainly be very neat,' agreed the Judge. 'But I don't get it. I'd have thought that a universe made like that would be very *boring* – not much variety. And yet I look around . . .'

'Exactly. All sorts of things going on. I often marvel about that,' said Phusis. 'A handful of laws and forces – possibly only one of each. You'd think all you had to do was to watch how ordinary, everyday objects behave in the home, and that would be that; one would then know all there was to be known – from the largest to the smallest. But it's not like that. If all you knew about was ordinary, everyday life, you'd have no idea what was going on at the large scale . . .'

'You mean the way space is pushing the galaxies apart,' the Judge suggested. 'And the way everything is governed by powerful gravity forces – forces that can stop clocks near black holes.'

'That's right. And not only that. You wouldn't know what was happening on the small scale either. Down there gravity hardly counts at all. And everything is uncertain – nothing can be predicted – unlike in ordinary life.'

'Hmmm. But it's the *same* laws that work on the small scale as on the big scale – and in ordinary life,' said the Judge.

'That's right. But the effects are different.'

Phusis began searching in her bag. She pulled out a painted wooden doll.

'I try to explain it to my children like this,' she said. 'Have you ever come across these? Russian dolls, they're called. Look.'

She pulled the top half of the doll. It came apart to reveal a second doll inside – a smaller one. She took it out, and did the same to this doll; it too split into two halves. Again she pulled out another doll – and another – and another. She set them out in a row in order of their size.

'There,' she said. 'That's how I see the world: it's actually worlds within worlds, within worlds. Except that the worlds are more interesting than these dolls. These dolls all look exactly alike – apart from their size. But with our universe, each of the inner worlds appears quite different from the larger, outer ones. And yet they are all made according to the same basic rules or laws.'

The Judge picked up a couple of the dolls and turned them over in his hands. He said nothing. He just looked at them thoughtfully.

The *964th* evening: 'Of course,' said Phusis, 'one of the big mysteries of the universe is: where did the laws come from?'

'How do you mean?' asked the Judge.

'Well, it takes intelligence to work out what the laws are, right?'

He nodded. 'A certain amount, yes.'

'Well, if it takes intelligence to understand what's going on in the world – did it not take an Intelligence

131

to set it up in the first place?'

He looked at her sharply. 'What exactly are you getting at?'

'Well, some of us think that God created everything. Did he? You'd know that sort of thing, of course.'

The Judge shifted uncomfortably, and shook his head.

'You don't?' asked Phusis. 'Oh. I'd have thought . . . You coming from the Federation of Universes, and all that . . . Shouldn't you . . .'

'Our records don't go back that far,' he said irritably. 'The Federation is quite new. We only date back 10,000 million years. Your universe goes back another 5,000 million years. It's very, *very* old. The sooner we tidy things up by getting rid of these . . .'

'Ah,' said Phusis. 'So God *could* have made it. Which brings us to the biggest mystery of all: *why* was the universe made?'

'*Why* was it made?'

'Yes. The fact that the universe has life in it. How did that come about?'

'That actually is a good question,' the Judge said. 'The vast majority of universes I have to deal with don't support life. That makes my job much easier, of course – there's no one to consult – I just have to make up my own mind as to whether the universe is out-of-date. But with universes like yours, it's a real bind. Nasty business: *life*. Makes things so much more difficult.'

Phusis was about to protest that life was anything but a 'nasty business', but decided to let it pass. 'Yes, well . . . It needed a whole lot of odd coincidences for life to come about . . .'

Over the following nights she described what these were.

She began by reminding him that the galaxies were all moving away from each other because of the way space was stretching. It all started with a Big Bang: all the matter that makes up the universe rushing out from a point. At this stage the matter was not in the form of stars and planets; it just consisted of simple gases. These gases had later to collect together to form the first stars. This was tricky. If the Big Bang had been ever so slightly more violent, the gases would have been thrown out so hard they would have all spread out through space too thinly to form stars. On the other hand, if the Big Bang had been ever so slightly less violent, stars would have formed all right, but the gravity forces would have brought them crashing back together in a Big Crunch before life had had a chance to evolve on any of the planets. So getting the violence of the Big Bang just right was the first problem to solve.

Next, one had somehow to take the simple gases and get their nuclei to stick together to form more interesting atoms – the sorts needed for making up living bodies. This was done inside stars – and very difficult it was too – to get them to stick properly.

Then, because you can't form living creatures inside stars where the temperatures can be tens of millions of degrees(!), there had to be a way by which stars could explode and throw out the newly formed atoms. Arranging *that* was a real headache.

Once this material had collected to form more stars like our Sun, and, for the first time, planets like the Earth, the process of evolution could get started – itself an amazing process for converting ordinary chemicals into wonderful creatures like human beings and the other animals, and the trees and plants.

This took a long time, as you can imagine. For all that time, the Sun had to keep steadily burning to provide the warmth necessary for life to develop. What a problem that was! The Sun uses the same nuclear fuel as a hydrogen bomb; it's a nuclear bomb going off *slowly*! That took some fixing.

'So,' concluded Phusis on the *996th* evening, 'the most unlikely thing about this universe is that it has succeeded, against all the odds, in producing life.'

'And what do you make of all of these "coincidences"?' asked the Judge.

'No one's sure. It could be that there are vast, vast numbers of universes, all built according to different laws. If so, most of them – the vast majority – won't support life. But there might be a few exceptions. These would be universes that happen, by chance, to satisfy all the right conditions. Ours would be one of them. I don't know, sir; you're better placed than us to know whether there's anything to that idea. Is there? Didn't I hear you say there were lots of universes . . .'

'Er . . . I'm afraid I can't help you there. I've already told you too much. The Federation is not at all keen on universes learning too much about each other. It prefers them – by and large – to mind their own business.'

'Quite. So, we don't have any way of learning about any other universes,' continued Phusis. 'Which brings us to the second idea: someone – I mean God – made the universe. And what's more, when he made it, he made it specially so it would produce living creatures. That's why the laws were fixed the way they were. If that's right, then we – and all other living creatures – *we* are the reason why the universe exists.'

'Yes, well as I said, our records don't go back far enough, so I can't confirm or deny that,' said the Judge. 'You'll just have to make up your own mind on that score.'

The 997th evening:

'Is anything the matter?' asked the Judge. 'You look a bit down in the dumps this evening.'

'Oh, it's nothing,' replied Phusis. 'It's just that horrid motorway. I told you about it, remember? Well, it's open now. The noise; you wouldn't believe it. We had no idea the sound of the traffic would carry so. When we saw the original plans, we thought that it wouldn't really affect us all that much. But you should hear it. Talk about a racket. And now the local paper has a story about a new housing development on the outskirts of the village. Green belt it was supposed to be, but with the motorway there now, they say the land isn't green belt any more; they're calling it "infill". I don't know; the village isn't what it used to be.'

She removed her coat, and settled down into her chair. 'Anyway,' she added, brightening up a little. 'Enough of that. Where did we get to yesterday?'

'Life. The way . . .'

'Ah, yes. Well, I suppose there's not much more to say on that subject. Of course, there wasn't always life in the universe; it took a long time to develop, and it won't last for ever.'

'Oh. Why not?' he asked.

'Everything's running down. The stars are using up their fuel. It'll take a long time, of course. But in the end they'll burn out. More and more matter gets sucked into black holes and crushed out of existence. The universe will eventually end up cold, lifeless and dead.'

The Judge looked grave. 'Which reminds me. All this talk about your universe being out-of-date. We must not overlook the *second* reason for removing it from our register: your universe is wearing out – it's getting into a mess.'

Phusis felt a chill run through her. 'Fool! Why did I bring up *that* subject,' she thought.

'It's like those videos you were showing me – a long time ago, remember?' he continued. 'We were trying to decide which way round they should be shown; which was the proper direction of time. It wasn't difficult to sort out, was it? We just looked for the way things were getting more and more messy and disordered – things getting broken, falling apart, that sort of thing. Cups getting smashed to pieces; it doesn't happen the other way round; broken pieces don't come together to form new cups. No, my dear.

Thank you. I was forgetting that.'

Phusis left the Red Lion that evening with a heavy heart.

The *998th* evening:

'It's true what we were saying last night – about most things wearing out, falling apart, getting disordered,' said Phusis. 'But there is one shining exception.'

'Oh. And what might that be?' he asked sceptically.

'Life,' she replied.

'That's not an exception. Living creatures grow old and wear out like everything else.'

'Ah, but what about the birth of a baby? At the birth of each baby, a fresh new living being is created! And what about evolution? Ever more complicated and wonderful new creatures evolving! The miracle of life continually swimming against a tide that does all in its power to sweep it away. I think that's pretty fantastic.'

The *999th* evening:

'And what of that mystery that seems to lie wholly beyond science to explain?' asked Phusis. 'The mystery of how it is living creatures have minds – they have thoughts and feelings. This pile of chemicals here,' she said, pointing to herself. 'It *knows* itself. It has a mind.'

'Why should you think that's a mystery?' asked the Judge. 'I thought scientists were learning more and more about the brain.'

'About the *brain*, yes. About its chemicals, about the electric currents that flow through it. Yes. And obviously these have some connection with a person's thoughts and feelings. But just because you understand what happens physically in the brain, that does not mean you understand the person's *mind*. Under a microscope the scientist sees chemicals; he doesn't see love, hate, anger, hunger, pleasure, decisions, hopes . . . Just chemicals moving about, that's all. Oh yes, there's a great mystery here. In the end, science has nothing to say about what it is to be a *person*. But being a person is what life is all about. And when the universe is destroyed, you will also be destroying persons. And that is a terrible, *terrible* thing to be doing.'

With that, Phusis suddenly gathered up her things, and fled in tears, slamming the door behind her.

The Judge said nothing. He just continued to sit there, staring thoughtfully at the flames in the hearth as they licked their way up the chimney.

On the *1000th* night, Phusis did not appear at all. The Judge was deeply disturbed. Was she ill? He sent the landlord to find out what the problem might be.

'She says she's not coming,' the landlord reported on his return.

'Not coming?' repeated the Judge. 'Why not? Is she not well?'

'Looked perfectly OK to me.'

'Where is she?'

'At home.'

'And she gave no reason?' asked the Judge.

'No.'

'Then go and tell her I want her over here – *immediately*.'

The landlord went off grumbling (though he was careful not to start grumbling until he was safely out of earshot of the Judge).

He was soon back again. 'It's like I said: she's not coming. She says she refuses to come . . .'

'*Refuses!*' spluttered the Judge. 'She . . . actually said that? She actually said "REFUSES"?' he thundered.

The landlord backed away towards the door in terror. He nodded as if his head was about to fall off.

'Right my girl, we'll soon see about that,' the Judge muttered. He whipped out his videophone. 'Fred!' he yelled at the screen. 'Dammit! Where is he? Never around when you . . . Ah! There you are. Where have you been? Never mind. The Schlurpit. Is it all set to go? If not, get your finger out. Tomorrow's the day.'

'Er, sorry, sir,' said Fred, not able to believe his ears.

'E-Day. Tomorrow!'

The Judge snapped the screen down. He looked up, his face black and menacing. He caught sight of the landlord huddled by the door. 'YOU!' he bellowed. 'What the hell are you doing here? GET OUT!'

The following morning, the Judge had his bags packed. For the very last time he sat in the saloon bar, quietly smoking his pipe. He had calmed down from the previous night, but was sad to think it all had to end like this.

'The taxi's here,' announced the landlord. 'I'll get your bags, sir.'

The Judge left his keys at the desk on the way out. He was about to get in the taxi, when he heard the sound of children. He could just make it out above the rumble of the motorway traffic that was now so obvious. The voices were coming from the other side of the green. It was break-time; the children were playing in the school yard.

'Wait here a minute,' he told the driver, and made his way across the green. He entered the yard; some children glanced at him briefly, but then resumed their games. Through the front door he went. He walked down the passage, stopping to admire the children's lively art work stuck up on the walls. Then he caught sight of Phusis through a half-opened door. She was sitting at her desk working.

'Oh,' she said, blushing slightly as he entered. 'I wasn't expecting . . .'

'Couldn't very well go without saying goodbye,' he said gruffly. 'We've known each other too long for that.'

She nodded. '1001 days,' she said. 'I've been counting.'

'Yes, I'm sure you have,' he said with a smile. 'Quite a feat. Not many can say they've saved an entire universe for 1001 days.' He paused. 'Which leaves me wondering . . . Why did you suddenly give up? Why didn't you come yesterday? That wasn't like you.'

'Oh, it wasn't really all that sudden. You see, all along one thing has been nagging away at me. All right, I never believed that just because the world is old it should be got rid of. It's a wonderful, wonderful world, and I hope even you realize that now. No. It was that second reason that bothered me: the fact that everything was getting into a mess – and it's our fault. Oh not the universe running down and all that; that's not going to happen for thousands of millions of years anyway. No, it's what we are doing to the place that's so awful. The more I told you about our world, and that wonderful mystery about the mind – the fact that we can be *aware* of the world, we can enjoy it; the more horrified I became. This is our home – the one God gave us – but look at what we're doing to it. We don't *deserve* a world like this. And then there are all the silly, silly things people get up to, even when they know they're about to die. Have you been reading the papers? And that horrible motorway spoiling the countryside. And then look at these . . .'

She passed him the pile of folders she was in the middle of marking. They were children's projects. He perched himself on a stool and started reading them.

As he did so, there was a timid knock on the door. 'Who is it?' called Phusis.

A little girl's head popped round the corner of the door.

'Yes? What is it, Sarah? Can't you see I'm busy?'

The head disappeared. There was giggling. Then a boy came in.

'Please, Miss.'

'Yes, Jamie.'

He came up to her and whispered, 'Please, Miss. We all want to know if this is . . . You know . . . HIM.'

She smiled. 'If you are referring to the Appeals Judge from Elsewhere, yes, this is he.'

The Judge looked up and grinned. 'Hi, so you're Jamie, are you? How are the experiments going these days? Got close to the speed of light yet?'

By now the other children had come surging in.

'Can we touch him, Miss?' asked Rebecca. 'You know, him not being real and all that.'

The Judge laughed. 'Yes, you can touch – by which I mean,' he added hastily, 'we can shake hands. I don't want any more slaps around the face.' He gave Phusis a knowing look.

'Do you like our projects?' asked Sarah.

'Yes, yes. Very nice,' he said. 'Are they all about the environment?'

'Yes,' piped up another voice. 'I did rain forests. Don't you think it's terrible what they're doing? Cutting down all the trees.'

'And what about the ozone layer?' said Jamie. 'Got a great big hole in it, it has. If we don't patch it up we'll all get skin cancer.'

'What I want to know,' said Sarah, 'is what's going to happen when all the oil is used up? How can we run ambulances and important things like that if there's no petrol? I reckon we shouldn't be wasting it on . . .'

'And then there's acid rain,' called out another. 'Have you read what I've written about that? There, it's that green folder . . .'

'What I want to know is what are they going to do

about the beaches. Do you know what was floating in the water next to me when I last . . .'

'*Not now*, Daniel,' interrupted Phusis. 'We've all heard about that – a dozen times.'

'Not the Judge. *He* hasn't heard it . . .'

A firm look from Phusis, and the boy fell silent.

'You see what I mean,' she said to the Judge quietly. 'Was it any surprise I got depressed reading all this. And it's all true; that's the awful thing – it's all true.'

'Yes, but it *won't* be,' declared Rebecca.

'It won't be?' asked the Judge. 'Er . . . What do you mean by that?'

'Well, you don't think we are going to behave like *that* do you!?' she said indignantly.

'Not likely,' joined in Jamie. 'You wait 'til I'm Prime Minister. I'll make all these things illegal. Anyone hurting the ozone layer will go straight to jail.'

'As for anyone polluting beaches,' shouted Daniel, 'When I'm in charge I'm going to stick their noses in . . .'

'DANIEL!' called out Phusis. 'I won't tell you again.'

As the noise subsided, a small voice spoke up, 'Sir. Mr Judge. Why do grown-ups do such naughty things? When *we* are grown up, we won't behave like that. We shall look after everything the way we ought to.'

The room fell quiet.

Phusis turned to the Judge. 'You ought to be going soon. I see you have a taxi waiting outside the Red Lion. But . . .'

'Yes?'

'Before you go – one last thing?'

'Go ahead.'

'Forget everything I have ever told you about this world. It was silly of me, trying to be clever – each day trying to win from you one further day of existence. Forget also the terrible mess we adults have got our planet into. The damage *can* be repaired, if only there are enough people who feel strongly enough about it. All right, that might not be the case with my generation; we grew up with greedy, selfish bad habits – habits that are hard to break. I am ashamed to admit that. But *their* generation might be different,' she said looking round at the children. 'They already know what the problems and dangers are – while they are young. So, they *might* turn out differently. The only way to find out, is to give them the chance. And that doesn't mean just one extra day, or 101 extra days or even 1001 extra days . . .'

The Judge thought long and hard.

A little girl whispered something to Phusis. 'Not now, Hannah.'

'Hmmm. What was that?' asked the Judge.

'Oh nothing,' said Phusis. 'Hannah just wanted to know, if she gave you a sweet, would you let her sit on your lap.'

The Judge grinned. 'Of course. Why not? Come on up.'

Hannah clambered on to his knee. The Judge quietly surveyed the sea of faces. The children looked back expectantly. After a while, he spoke: 'Your universe is a very old one. Usually we . . . we make

an end of such universes. It's for the best; it makes room for new ones. But your teacher, Phusis, has shown me how your universe is really rather special. But the trouble is that you . . . er, not *you* . . . I mean the grown-ups – they aren't looking after it properly. Now *you* say you will behave differently – when it's your turn to make all the big decisions. But how do I know that will be true? How do I know that you won't be just as greedy and selfish as them?'

There was silence. Then Chris spoke up; he was one of the older boys – one of those soon to leave the village school for the big school in town.

'You don't,' he said. 'You can't be sure. Even *we* can't be sure how we shall turn out in later years. But we deserve a chance. That's only fair, isn't it? You will have to trust us. It's as simple as that: you will have to trust us.'

The Judge looked at him long and hard, then at the other children, then at Phusis. Suddenly his face broke out into a smile.

'OK. OK. I've decided,' he said. 'Have it your way. There will not be an E-Day. No extermination.'

The children cheered. 'Can we go and tell our Mums?' they cried.

The Judge nodded. 'Why not?'

They all rushed out of the room – all except Hannah, who was content to remain where she was.

'Remember to cross the road carefully,' called out Phusis after them.

The Judge sighed. 'Mind you, when I say "no

extermination", I mean Fred will not exterminate them. That doesn't mean they can't exterminate themselves.'

He looked down at Hannah, munching on a mouthful of sweets. 'Hey, I think you've had enough of these for one day,' he said. 'You've got to start looking after your teeth again.'

Epilogue

Only a Beginning . . .

Before leaving the universe, the Judge called a meeting of all the clever science professors in the world.

'Phusis has shown me that this universe of yours is really quite remarkable,' he told them. 'I think it's only right that everyone should hear about it. So, I want you to listen carefully to all she has to say, and write it down in a book for others to read.'

The professors looked at each other, and sniggered.

'Excuse me, sir,' said one of them – a particularly famous scientist, one who had won lots of prizes and awards for his work. 'You don't seem to realize: we have already done this.'

'You have?' said the Judge. 'Oh. Good.'

'Yes, we call them *physics* books. In case you are wondering, the word *physics* comes from the feminine Greek word, *phusis*, meaning "nature" or "the natural order" . . .'

'All right, all right. Stop showing off,' the Judge said irritably. 'Where are these books? I'd like to have a look at them.'

'Certainly.'

And they brought forward a pile of huge books. The Judge sat for several minutes leafing through them. He looked up sharply.

'Is this meant to be a joke or something? I can't make head nor tail of any of them,' he said angrily. 'They seem to be written in a foreign language.'

The professors regarded him scornfully.

'It might seem that way to you,' their spokesman smirked. 'In fact what you are referring to is *mathematics*. We write our physics down in a mathematical language. You can take it from us, it is much the best language to use when discussing physics; it's so precise, so accurate in its meaning.'

The professors all smiled at each other, and nodded in agreement.

'Oh, I see,' said the Judge. 'And do many people know this language?'

At this the spokesman shifted uncomfortably. He glanced anxiously across at his colleagues. 'Well, sir, not as many as we would like – shall I put it that way.'

'I don't care how you put it. Do ordinary people – not professors – I mean *normal* people; do *they* understand it?'

'Well, I'm sure they *could*, if only they would try . . .'

'And another thing,' interrupted the Judge. 'The parts of this I *can* understand – I don't like the sound of them. They're so smug; so arrogant . . .'

'Smug?'

'Anyone reading them would think everything was cut-and-dried; that you know all the answers; that there's nothing left for anyone else – the young people – to discover. But that's not what I got from Phusis. This world of yours is much more interesting than that; much more deep and mysterious.'

The Judge slammed the books shut, and shoved them back into the arms of the professors.

'No,' he declared. 'They won't do. They're not what I had in mind at all.'

A gleam came into his eye. 'I know,' he said, 'I am issuing a decree – a condition for not exterminating your universe. From now on, all the science professors in the world must take lessons from Phusis on how to teach physics in an interesting way.'

'WHAT?' they all exclaimed in horror. 'We . . . *we* are to take lessons? But we are PROFESSORS!'

'That's right. You can sit over there in the school – alongside the children.'

'But . . . But we wouldn't all fit in. There are too many of us . . .'

'Then you will have to take it in turns, won't you!' roared the Judge. 'For goodness' sake, work it out for yourself.'

The professors departed, shaking their heads.

Later that day, two figures sat on the bench by the pond on the green.

'So, this really is goodbye, Phusis,' said the Judge. 'But . . . One thing I'm not sure about: you not coming to see me that time. Had you *really* given up hope? Or was that just your cunning way of getting me to come over and meet your children . . .?'

Phusis was about to reply, but he raised his hand to stop her.

'No,' he said. 'Don't tell me. Let's just say that's another of your little mysteries.'

She smiled. 'If I may,' she said, 'there's one thing I'd like to ask you before you go.'

'Oh. What's that?'

'Well, if God created our universe, and other universes, how come . . .'

'. . . it's the Federation that gets rid of them?' he asked.

'Yes. Where does the Federation come into it all?'

'That's an interesting question,' said the Judge with a knowing smile. 'It's one I have often wondered about. Do you know what I reckon? I shouldn't be telling you this,' he whispered, looking furtively over his shoulder, 'but I reckon the Federation is just a front organization.'

'A what?'

'A front organization. Er . . . a set-up for hiding who is really in charge – the one who really pulls the strings. I reckon there's someone behind the scenes who actually runs the Federation – gets them to dispose of universes that he has no further use for. That way he can still leave everybody to make up their own minds as to whether he exists or not. Neat, eh? Anyway, that's between you and me.'

Peep! Peep! . . . Peep! Peep!

'OK, Fred. I'm on my way.'

'Huh. I've heard that before,' replied Fred.

'No, no. I mean it this time. Look. There, behind me; that's my taxi. Hey, that's a thought. How long's that been there? I hope I've left myself with enough . . .' He fumbled in his pocket . . .

'Well, that's great, sir,' said Fred. 'Tell me, have you seen this?' On the screen of the videophone he could be seen holding up a long sheet of computer output. 'How about *that*?' he cried excitedly. 'Straight from Headquarters. A 1001-day back-log of clapped-out universes! Ha! Now I ask you: there's got to be a bit of the old overtime for Fred in all that lot, eh? Be seeing yer!'

That was the last Phusis saw or heard of Fred. The taxi driver did get paid all right. The children often asked about the Man from Elsewhere; they thought the professors were quite good at lessons – but rubbish when it came to games at break-time. The landlord of the Red Lion made a fortune charging double for the room where his 'old friend, the Judge' stayed. The Judge himself got home safely, complained about the hologram and got a replacement (he was lucky – the old one had a three-year guarantee), and immediately started to give his special kind of attention to the universes on the Federation's list. As for the future of our world – well that depends . . .